Instructor's Manual

to accompany

Anatomy & Physiology Laboratory Manual

Eric Wise
Santa Barbara City College

Boston Burr Ridge, IL Dubuque, IA Madison, WI New York San Francisco St. Louis
Bangkok Bogotá Caracas Lisbon London Madrid
Mexico City Milan New Delhi Seoul Singapore Sydney Taipei Toronto

WCB/McGraw-Hill

A Division of The ***McGraw-Hill*** *Companies*

Instructor's Manual to accompany
ANATOMY AND PHYSIOLOGY LABORATORY MANUAL

1 2 3 4 5 7 8 9 0 QPD/QPD 9 0 9 8

ISBN 0-697-20555-X

www.mhhe.com

BIOGRAPHY

Eric Wise lives in Santa Barbara, California with his wife, Mary, and two daughters, Sarah and Caitlin. He is a tenured faculty member at Santa Barbara City College teaching Anatomy, Anatomy and Physiology, Environmental Biology, Freshwater Biology and Physical Anthropology. Eric has been teaching since 1981 and has a Masters degree in Biology from California Polytechnic State University, San Luis Obispo and bachelors degrees in Biology, Botany and French from Humboldt State University, California.

CONTENTS

INTRODUCTION

This instructor's resource manual was written to assist you in the preparation of the lab portion of the course. It serves to coordinate the labs with the ordering of material, aid the lab technician in preparing material for the lab, provide a detailed list of preparations and sources for ordering, and instructional aids in the running of the lab. This manual also provides answers to the review questions at the back of each exercise.

The lab manual contains 47 exercises that cover the breadth of human anatomy and physiology. The lab manual can be used for courses that are a year in length or one term courses (quarter or semester). Each exercise can be used in its entirety or shortened depending on the time available or according to your interest. Labs vary in terms of equipment. Some exercises may need to be modified or deleted entirely due to the physical constraints of the institution. The text is written for students who are introductory students to the material and may have little or no chemistry background.

Orders must be made ahead of time for items such as sterilized blood, live frogs, enzymes and other materials for the preparation of solutions. Many supply companies will take orders early and ship material to arrive at the scheduled time. As labs are being prepared specific quantities of materials need to be prepared. A general rule of thumb is to calculate the total amount of material that will be used in lab and double that amount.

Materials listed in this lab manual are generally indicated as per student, per table (assuming a table of 4), or per lab section (25 students). Test all reagents and experiments prior to trying them in lab. Note any modifications to the experiments for future use. I would be very happy to hear from you regarding comments or suggestions concerning the lab. You can contact me through WCB/McGraw Hill or at Santa Barbara City College.

Instructor's resources such as 35 mm slide reviews at the end of lab, videos, laser disc presentations, additional texts or illustrations add to students comprehension of the material. Some students want to go beyond the material at hand and available references are wonderful to have in the lab.

Safety in the Lab

Safety in the lab is one of the primary concerns of any instructor teaching anatomy and physiology. Safety guidelines are printed in the lab manual and should be thoroughly covered by the instructor prior to beginning the lab. Several potential hazards occur in the lab including:

1. Sharp objects such as broken glassware, razor blades, scalpel blades and other potentially dangerous cutting or puncturing objects. Proper disposal of sharp objects is essential as is the handling of these objects.
2. Infectious diseases—students should wear gloves and protective eyewear when handling bodily fluids. Students should handle only their own fluids unless closely supervised by the instructor or other qualified personnel. Students need to be prepared to work with infectious agents. Those students entering the health profession will probably encounter potentially lethal diseases in their profession and an early protocol that influences safety cannot be stressed enough. Even if you know material is non-pathogenic, students should treat it as if it is. Material that has come into contact with bodily fluids must be placed in a 10% bleach solution or deposited in a sharps container.
3. Disposal of animal wastes—institutions with incinerators may take animal wastes including local universities and animal control facilities. Material preserved with formaldehyde should not be disposed of in local landfills.
4. Flames or hot surfaces—Most of the experiments requiring heating in these exercises can be done using hot plates. It is important to use heat-proof glassware on the hot plates. Generally glass fingerbowls and household jars are not heat proof and should not be heated on hot plates.
5. Toxic materials—Some of the material in lab is very toxic. Students should not eat food in lab and make sure they wash their hands after handling material in lab. Spills must be cleaned-up immediately. All reagents used in lab that are potentially dangerous should have a manufacturers safety data sheet (MSDS) that can be consulted if spills occur.

This lab manual was written in conjunction with *Anatomy and Physiology: The Unity of Form and Function* by Kenneth S. Saladin. I have provided correlations between the Saladin text and the lab manual. The lab manual, however, can be used with any standard college anatomy and physiology text.

Chapters in *Anatomy and Physiology: The Unity of Form and Function* by Kenneth S. Saladin	**Corresponding Exercises in *Anatomy and Physiology Laboratory Manual* by Eric Wise**
Ch 1 Major Themes of Anatomy and Physiology	1 Scientific Method and Measurement
Atlas A General Orientation to Human Anatomy	2 Organs, Systems and Organization of the Body
Ch 2 Matter and Energy	No corresponding exercise
Ch 3 The Molecules of Life	No corresponding exercise
Ch 4 Cellular Form and Function	4 Cell Structure and Function
	5 Some Functions of Cell Membranes
Ch 5 Genetics and Cellular Function	5 Some Functions of Cell Membranes
Ch 6 Histology	6 Tissues
Ch 7 The Integumentary System	7 Integumentary System
Ch 8 Bone Tissue	8 Introduction to the Skeletal System
Ch 9 The Skeletal System	9 Appendicular Skeleton
	10 Axial Skeleton—Vertebrae, Ribs, Sternum, Hyoid
	11 Axial Skeleton—Skull
Ch 10 Joints	12 Articulations
Ch 11 The Muscular System	13 Introduction to the Study of Muscles and Muscles of the Shoulder and Arm
	14 Muscles of the Forearm and Hand
	15 Muscles of the Hip and Thigh
	16 Muscles of the Leg and Foot
	17 Muscles of the Head and Neck
	18 Muscles of the Trunk
Ch 12 Muscular Tissue	19 Muscle Physiology
Ch 13 Nervous Tissue	20 Introduction to the Nervous System
Ch 14 The Central Nervous System	21 Structure and Function of the Brain and Cranial Nerves
	22 Structure and Function of the Spinal Cord and Nerves
Ch 15 The Peripheral Nervous System and Reflexes	23 Nervous System Physiology—Stimuli and Reflexes

Chapter	Exercise
Ch 16 Sense Organs	24 Introduction to Sensory Organs
	25 Taste and Smell
	26 Eye and Vision
	27 Ear, Hearing, and Equilibrium
Ch 17 The Endocrine System	28 Endocrine System
Ch 18 The Circulatory System: Blood	29 Blood Cells
	30 Blood Tests and Typing
Ch 19 The Circulatory System: The Heart	31 Structure of the Heart
	32 Electrical Conductivity of the Heart
	33 Functions of the Heart
Ch 20 The Circulatory System: Vessels and Circulation	34 Introduction to the Blood Vessels and Blood Arteries of the Upper Body
	35 Arteries of the Lower Body
	36 Veins and Fetal Circulation
	38 Blood Vessels and Blood Pressure
Ch 21 The Lymphatic and Immune Systems	37 Functions of Vessels, Lymphatic System
Ch 22 The Respiratory System	39 Structure of the Respiratory System
	40 Respiratory Function, Breathing, Respiration
Ch 23 The Urinary System	44 Urinary System
	45 Urinalysis
Ch 24 Water, Electrolyte, and Acid-Base Balance	No corresponding exercise
Ch 25 The Digestive System	42 Anatomy of the Digestive System
Ch 26 Nutrition and Metabolism	43 Digestive Physiology
Ch 27 The Male Reproductive System	46 Male Reproductive System
Ch 28 The Female Reproductive System	47 Female Reproductive System
Ch 29 Human Development	No corresponding exercise
No corresponding chapter	41 Physiology of Exercise
No corresponding chapter	3 Microscopy

Virtual Physiology Lab CD-ROM
Correlations with *Anatomy and Physiology Laboratory Manual*
by
Eric Wise

Exercises in *Anatomy and Physiology Laboratory Manual* by Eric Wise	***Virtual Physiology Lab CD-ROM* Number and Title**
5 Some Functions of Cell Membranes	9: Diffusion, Osmosis, and Tonicity
19 Muscle Physiology	3: Frog Muscle
20 Introduction to the Nervous System	1: Action Potential
	2: Synaptic Transmission
32 Electrical Conductivity of the Heart	5: Electrocardiogram
33 Functions of the Heart	4: Effects of Drugs on the Frog Heart
40 Respiratory Function, Breathing, Respiration	6: Pulmonary Function
41 Physiology of Exercise	7: Respiration and Exercise
43 Digestive Physiology	8: Digestion of Fat
	10: Enzyme Characteristics

EXERCISE 1
SCIENTIFIC METHOD AND MEASUREMENT

INTRODUCTION

This lab introduces the student to the fields of anatomy and physiology and discusses science as a general field of study. Although the "scientific method" is not a universally prescribed dogma of experimental technique, the goals of valid science do have criteria of experimental repeatability and prior publication rights that are followed by members of the community.

Terms such as *hypothesis*, *control group*, *experimental group*, *theory* and *law* can help students distinguish the specific parameters of scientific study from what is commonly perceived as science by the layperson. Another important area for discussion is the topic of honesty in science. Recent court cases involving interpretation of data by "paid consultants" has blurred the objectivity of the scientific experience yet good discussions can be had by opening-up the topic of honesty in the commercial development of new drugs and the need for honest appraisal of one's work when the efforts of science are used for purposes that concern the health or well-being of people.

The other main part of the lab is to introduce the student to the idea of data collection, working with data, graphing results and interpreting the data in a very simple format. Some students will have no difficulty with the numerical portion of the exercise while others may feel very frustrated. It is a good time to make an early evaluation of students' relationship to math and the potential need for an augmentation of their efforts in math.

TIME 1-1.5 hours

MATERIALS

Meter stick (1 per pair of students)

TEXT ANSWERS

1 centigram

1 kilosecond

1 decameter

1 nanoliter

4.3×10^6

3.4×10^{-5}

2.2×10^3

1.9×10^{-3}

REVIEW ANSWERS

1. How would you write 0.000345 liters in scientific notation?

   Ans: 3.45×10^{-4} *liters*

2. How many milligrams are there in 4.5 kilograms?

   Ans: 4,500,000 milligrams

3. How many meters is 250 millimeters?

   Ans: 0.25 meters

4. If you were to do a new experiment, what do you estimate the relationship between the length of the arm and the overall height of an individual?

   Ans: The greater the height the greater the arm length. This should correlate to the answers obtained in the experiments in lab.

5. In the case of arm length and overall height, which is the independent variable and which is the dependent variable?

   Ans: In this case, height is the independent variable and arm length is the dependent variable.

EXERCISE 2
ORGANS, SYSTEMS, AND ORGANIZATION OF THE BODY

INTRODUCTION

In this exercise the field of anatomy is introduced with directional terms and general discussions of the systemic study of anatomy. Comparisons of organ systems with regional anatomy is useful for students and having students list what organs belong to what system and what constitutes an organ is of benefit.

When discussing the atomic level of organization having available MRIs from local hospitals or physicians allows students to examine the importance of anatomic study from various perspectives and technologies. It is also important to compare directional terms for quadrupeds with those for humans as *superior* and *inferior* are specific terms for humans. The terms *anterior/ventral* and *posterior/dorsal* are synonymous in humans while the anterior end of a quadruped is towards the nose while the dorsal side is along the vertebral column.

Planes of sectioning are also important concepts in the study of anatomy. Illustrations of organs that have been sectioned or thin sections of organs embedded in plastic make good tools for discussing sectioning planes. Likewise the use of torso models for the discussion of body cavities provides a good visual medium for demonstration.

Most students have an intuitive sense and some familiarity with the regions of the body. Particular notice should be given to the specific use of "arm" (from the shoulder to the elbow) and "leg" (from the knee to the ankle) used in anatomy. Descriptions of the abdominal region are also reasonably comprehensible. The term "hypochondriac" comes from the Greek words meaning "under the cartilage". In earlier times the hypochondriac area was thought to be the center of melancholy.

TIME 1-1.5 hours

MATERIALS

Models of human torso (1 or more per lab)
Charts of human torso (1 per lab)

REVIEW ANSWERS

1. Pain that stems from the appendix might be felt in what quadrant of the abdomen?

   Ans: Lower right

2. In terms of up and down, the umbilicus is __________ to the sternum.

   Ans: inferior

3. In terms of closeness to the trunk, the elbow is __________ to the fingers.

   Ans: proximal

4. In terms of nearness to the surface, the liver is ___________ to the skin.

   Ans: deep

5. In terms of front to back, the nipples are ___________ to the shoulder blades.

   Ans: anterior

6. The kidney belongs to the ______________ system.

Ans: urinary

7. The liver belongs to the ______________ system.

Ans: digestive

8. The spleen belongs to the ______________ system.

Ans: lymph

9. If you were to sit on a horse's back you would be on the ________ aspect of the horse.

a. anterior b. ventral c. posterior d. dorsal

Ans: d. dorsal

EXERCISE 3
MICROSCOPY

INTRODUCTION

Microscopy and beginning students are an interesting combination. In any introductory science class there are usually students who have had absolutely no experience with microscopes, those who have had some experience with microscopes (but the experience has been limited or with other types of microscopes than those found in this particular lab), and perhaps some with quite a bit of microscope experience. Another interesting factor is the great reluctance on the part of many students to admit that they do not know how to use a microscope (or know how to use it well).

It is worth the effort to take the entire class and provide them with a demonstration of the microscope before letting them actually use the instruments. Frequently when students have a microscope at their desks and you are lecturing they pay no attention to the lecture but rather fiddle with the mechanisms in front of them. Once they have been shown the microscope and learn the parts then they seem to have an easier time with the exercise.

Discussions about care of the microscope vary from instructor to instructor but I think that you cannot assume that your students will know anything about microscope care unless you provide them with specific guidelines. Some of these are listed in this exercise. Likewise the knowledge of the parts of the microscope is important. Students who know the structure of the microscope will have a good understanding of the functions of the parts. Microscope models vary by manufacturer so you may wish to provide students with a labeled illustration of the microscopes in your particular lab.

To understand the field of view I like to have students measure the field of view directly under low power. You can take standard metric rulers and place several of them on a photocopy machine and run a piece of overhead transparency acetate through the machine. Cut the acetate sheets into small (10 - 15 cm) sections. Students can place the thin strips of acetate on their microscope stages, examine them under low power and directly measure the field of view.

Once they have obtained this value they can switch to the next higher objective lens and make their count to determine the diameter of the field of view. The diameter should decrease in inverse proportion to the magnification of the lens. Thus if the diameter is 4 mm at 40 × then the diameter should be 0.4 of that (or 1.6 mm) at 100 ×. The magnification 100 × is 2.5 times greater than 40 × so the field of view is 2.5 times smaller.

When working with students in lab it is good to have them get started on their microscope work and then walk around the room to see if the students have put the microscope slides on the stage correctly. Determine if they know how to adjust the light, move the slide around, focus correctly, etc. Sometimes students will not ask for help but it is apparent from a little observation that they need it.

Students usually have no problem with the preparation of wet mounts other than sometimes trapping air bubbles under the coverslip or not putting on a coverslip at all. Prepared slides are easy to begin with, though more expensive to replace than the wet mounts prepared in lab.

TIME 1.5 hours

MATERIALS

Light microscopes
Transparent rulers or sections of overhead acetates of rulers
Glass microscope slides
Coverslips
Lens paper for microscope lenses
Kimwipes ® or other cleaning paper
Lens cleaner
Squeeze water bottle (1 per table)
1% methylene blue solution (1 part methylene blue crystals in 100 parts absolute alcohol)
Toothpicks
Histological slides of kidney, stomach or liver

REVIEW ANSWERS

1. Ocular lenses are typically 10 × If the objective lenses of a microscope are 5, 17, and 35 respectively what would all of the total magnifications be if you used these lenses sequentially?

   a. ______________ *Ans: 50*

   b. ______________ *Ans: 170*

   c. ______________ *Ans 350*

2. What is the function of the iris diaphragm of the microscope?

   Ans: The iris diaphragm regulates the amount of light that strikes the condensor lens and subsequently illuminates the specimen.

3. If the diameter of the field of view is 5.6 mm at 40 × what would the diameter be at 80 ×?

   Ans: 2.8 mm

4. Label the parts of the microscope illustrated.

   A. Ocular lens *B. Body*

   C. Arm *D. Coarse focus knob*

   E. Stage *F. Objective lens*

EXERCISE 4
CELL STRUCTURE AND FUNCTION

INTRODUCTION

The importance of learning about cells in anatomy and physiology is fundamental to the discipline. Students can understand the reliance of the complete organism on cellular functions as well as medical research into cellular and molecular processes in an attempt to understand and treat disease. At the beginning of this understanding is the study of cellular structures including the plasma membrane, the cytoplasm and the nucleus.

Membrane structure and function are often difficult for the beginning student to understand. The idea that the membrane is a dynamic structure, more like a soap bubble than a brick wall, is often useful for the student.

The nature of the cytoplasm is also important in the initial discussion of the cell. Students can get lost in the new vocabulary and become focused on long, complex words (e.g. endoplasmic reticulum) to the point that they ignore the function of the organelle. Some students cannot easily grasp what they cannot see so visual images are important in learning about cells.

Finally the nature of how cells replicate themselves is also an area that needs care in presentation. The terms mitosis and the cell cycle are frequently used interchangeably yet the cell cycle consists of mitosis (nuclear division), cytokinesis (cytoplasmic division) and the events of interphase (including DNA replication). When students have the opportunity to use their hands and make mitosis happen in lab they frequently understand the process much more clearly than from what is obtained in standard lecture formats. The science lab becomes important in the overall pedagogy involved in reaching out to students who have different learning styles. Sometimes a few extra-credit points for a successful demonstration of mitosis provides great motivation for students' participation in the process.

TIME 2 hours

MATERIALS

Models or charts of animal cells
Electron micrographs of cells or textbook with electron micrographs
Prepared slides of whitefish blastula
Microscopes
Modeling clay (Plasticine) (2 colors each per table)
Marbles (4 per table)

REVIEW ANSWERS

1. Name the phases of the cell cycle as illustrated.

a. Late telophase and Cytokinesis *b. Prophase*

c. Metaphase *d. Anaphase*

e. Interphase

2. Name the organelles as illustrated.

a. Golgi body

b. Mitochondrion

c. Smooth endoplasmic reticulum

d. Rough endoplasmic reticulum

e. Ribosome

3. Fill in the chart below for the name, structure or function of the organelles.

Organelle	**Function**	**Structure**
Ribosome	protein production for use inside of the cell	not membrane-bound
Smooth ER	*detoxifies*	no attached ribosomes
Golgi apparatus	packages and transports material	vesicles on organelle
Mitochondrion	produces energy for the cell	*has cristae*
Rough ER	protein production for use outside of the cell	*with attached ribosomes*

EXERCISE 5
SOME FUNCTIONS OF CELL MEMBRANES

INTRODUCTION

Another important hands-on exercise for students in the understanding of diffusion and osmosis is to perform experiments of these events in lab. The driving force for diffusion or osmosis is kinetic energy and thus the demonstration of Brownian motion provides a clear visualization of the energy that affects molecules. Fat droplets are large and relatively light when compared to a dilute India ink solution (which is frequently used to demonstrate Brownian motion). Diffusion of materials can be seen by adding a dye crystal to water. Students should be able to apply their knowledge from the Brownian motion demonstration to the diffusion experiment.

The use of potassium permanganate, methylene blue and potassium dichromate solutions diffusing through a liquid medium (agar gels being liquids) provides for a comparison between molecules of greater mass and those of lesser mass. It is important that the students do NOT twist the drinking straws as twisting the straws can lead to fractures in the agar gel. The dye moves into the fracture making diffusion rates hard to measure.

The demonstration on osmosis is best done by the instructor. Keeping the thistle tube from leaking can be somewhat problematic. Molasses or colored sugar water can be used to demonstrate the principle of water moving from hypotonic solutions to hypertonic solutions. This demonstration can be set up as students prepare their own osmosis experiments. The dialysis tubing can be left to soak at the beginning of the lab period, though sometimes the tubing opens easier if it has been soaking for an hour or more before lab. It helps to color coordinate the sugar solutions used by the students and make sure that the students mark each of the beakers taking care not to confuse the dialysis bags.

Once the idea of osmosis has been grasped the implications of osmosis and living membranes can be demonstrated with the use of a small amount of mammal blood obtained from the local veterinarian. The blood cells are hypertonic to distilled water and should swell and burst (lyse) when they are placed in pure water. In isotonic solutions cells should retain their normal shape and those cells in 5% saline should crenate as they are hypotonic to the saline solution. Latex gloves should be worn as a precaution to any potential mammalian diseases that might be in the donated blood.

The filtration experiment can be done as a demonstration or as a part of the students' experiment. Charcoal should not pass through the membrane yet the molecules of copper sulfate and starch are small enough to pass through the pores of the membrane. The filtration rate can be measured and varies on how much liquid is in the funnel or how much the pores are clogged.

TIME 2 hours

MATERIALS

Brownian Motion

Whole milk—100 mls in a dropper bottle (1 bottle per table)

Fat testing solution (1% Sudan III solution) in a dropper bottle (1 per lab)

Microscopes

Microscope slides

Coverslips
Vegetable oil or light household oil in dropper bottles (1 per table)
Hot plate

Diffusion Demo

Potassium permanganate crystals (1 small, shallow jar)
100 ml beaker
2 Liters of water in small necked flask

Diffusion

Agar plates (1 per table)
0.01 M potassium permanganate solution in dropper bottles
0.01 M methylene blue solution in dropper bottles
0.01 M potassium dichromate solution in dropper bottles
plastic drinking straws
fine probe or small forceps
warming tray

Osmosis Demonstration

Thistle tube
Dialysis tubing (to fit over the open end of the thistle tube)
Rubber band or thread
1 small bottle of molasses or concentrated sucrose solution (20%)
Ring stand and clamp (1 per lab)
250 ml beaker (1 per lab)
500 mls of distilled water

Osmosis experiment

Four strips of 20 cm long dialysis tubing (per table)
Four 200 ml beakers (1 set of 4 per table)
A small ball of string
Scissors (1 pair per table)
Four solutions (2 liters each) of 0%, 5%, 15% and 30% sucrose
4 Balances
4 Towels (placed near balances)
10 ml pipettes (1 per table)
Pipette pumps (1 per table)

Osmosis and Living Cells

Clean glass microscope slides (1 box per table)
Coverslips (1 box per table)
5 ml of mammal blood (available at local veterinarian's office)
Distilled water in small dropper bottle (1 per table)
0.9% saline solution in dropper bottle (1 per table)
5% saline solution in dropper bottles (1 per table)
Latex or plastic gloves (small, medium, large)

Filtration

Filter paper—sized to fit appropriate funnel (1 per table)
Funnel (1 per table)
10 ml graduated cylinder (1 per table)
250 ml beaker (1 per table)
Iodine in dropper bottles (1 per table)
Filtration solution—500 mls of 1% starch, 1% charcoal and 1% copper sulfate
(consists of 5 grams of each in 500 mls water)
Stopwatch or clock with secondhand (1 per table)

REVIEW ANSWERS

1. What effect would lowering the temperature to absolute zero (-273° C) have on Brownian motion?

   Ans: Brownian motion would stop.

2. Given you have two different molecules, one of 230 molecular weight and one of 415 molecular weight, which one would diffuse the farthest if they were both allowed to diffuse for the same length of time?

   Ans: The one of 230 molecular weight. Lighter particles diffuse farther.

3. If a dialysis bag of 20% sugar solution was placed in a beaker of 40% sugar solution and allowed to remain there for a few minutes, would the solution in the bag be hypertonic or hypotonic to the solution in the beaker?

   Ans: The bag solution is hypotonic to the beaker solution.

   Would the water flow into or out of the bag?

   Ans: The water would flow out of the bag.

4. What would happen to the filtration rate if you were to apply pressure from a water hose to the filtration system?

   Ans: The filtration rate would increase.

   What might happen to the filtration membrane if the water pressure was too high?

   Ans: The membrane might split or the pressure might force particles through the membrane that would not normally pass through.

   Why might this be of concern to people that have both kidney disease and high blood pressure?

   Ans: High blood pressure is deleterious to kidneys as it damages the filtering membrane of the kidney.

EXERCISE 6
TISSUES

INTRODUCTION

Histology is something that many students appreciate after they graduate from anatomy and physiology and begin working in the field. Several factors are at work that make the study of histology more difficult than other areas of anatomy and physiology. The use of microscopes can pose problems to students, most of what students see is unfamiliar, appearing as pink and blue stuff, and the beginning students usually have a limited appreciation of the extent to which the allied health field focuses on disease states at the level of the cell or molecule.

If students do not feel comfortable using the microscope (Exercise 3) then this is a good time to help them work through and refine their technique. Having students show you what they see is critical in your evaluation of how well they are doing. Students can benefit tremendously by drawing the material seen through the microscope. Many students are embarrassed to draw and encouragement from the instructor for their efforts is often helpful.

If there is not enough time for students to see all that is available in this lab part of this lab and the next lab can be combined. The combination of connective tissue and the integumentary system works well.

A word of caution for testing a student's histological knowledge. If students are looking at tissues for the first time they often rely on the knowledge gained from the slide that they selected in lab. You may wish to have them examine several slides. As you test them try to select a representative slide from the same source as the students. Small differences in slides (such as variations in stain) may confuse students who have had minimal exposure to the material.

TIME 3-4 hours to examine slides and make drawings, 2-3 hours just to examine slides

MATERIALS

Microscopes
Colored pencils (assortment for drawing)

Epithelial Tissue Slides

1. Simple squamous epithelium
2. Simple cuboidal epithelium
3. Simple columnar epithelium
4. Pseudostratified ciliated columnar epithelium
5. Stratified squamous epithelium
6. Transitional epithelium

Muscular Tissue Slides

7. Skeletal muscle
8. Cardiac muscle

9. Smooth muscle
10. All three muscle types

Nervous Tissue Slides

11. Spinal cord smear

Connective Tissue Slides

12. Dense connective tissue
13. Elastic connective tissue
14. Reticular connective tissue
15. Loose (areolar) connective tissue
16. Adipose tissue
17. Ground bone
18. Hyaline cartilage
19. Fibrocartilage
20. Elastic cartilage
21. Blood

REVIEW ANSWERS

1. Label the following photomicrographs by using the terms provided.

    Collagenous fibers, elastic fibers, macrophages, fibroblasts
    Cilia, basement membrane, nucleus
    Intercalated discs, striations, nucleus
    Nerve cell body, glial cells

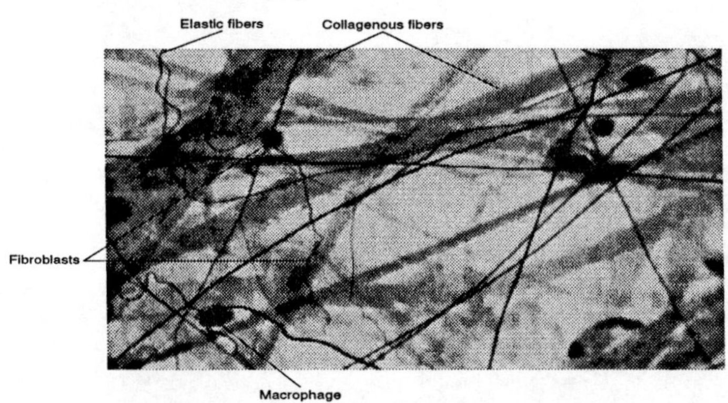

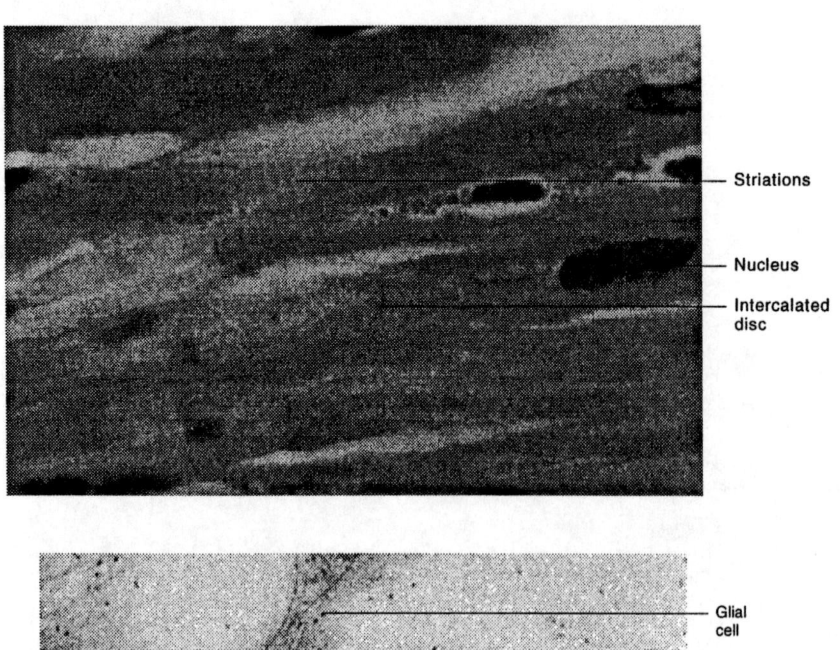

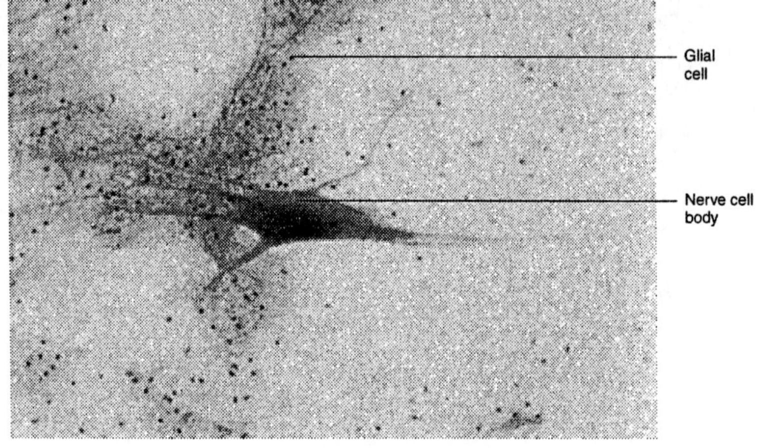

2. How do the groupings of cells differ between hyaline cartilage and fibrocartilage? In which specific tissue are the cells in pairs? In which specific tissue are the cells in fours or fives?

   Ans: Cells are aligned in rows of 4-5 in fibrocartilage and are typically paired in hyaline cartilage.

EXERCISE 7
INTEGUMENTARY SYSTEM

INTRODUCTION

If students have not had an introduction to the microscope they should review Exercise 3 prior to starting this exercise. The integumentary system can be studied from the standpoint of the two main layers of the integument, the epidermis and dermis, followed by the detailed examination of each layer as well as the non-integumentary hypodermis. All of the epidermal layers are evident in sections of thick skin with the stratum lucidum being present only in thick skin. Discussions of the role of melanocytes and melanin can precede or follow the observation of skin from light and dark individuals.

Models of the integumentary system are useful as are drawings of hair roots in hair follicles at various angles of sectioning. Students frequently have initial difficulty in locating sebaceous glands and sudoriferous glands yet, once they have been accurately identified, students can easily distinguish one from the other. Sometimes drawings help to get the student to slow down and observe more carefully.

TIME 1-1.5 hours

MATERIALS

Models and charts of the integumentary system

Prepared microscope slides of:

- Thick skin (with pacinian corpuscles)
- Hair follicles
- Pigmented and non-pigmented skin

Microscopes (1 per student or per pair)

REVIEW ANSWERS

1. Distinguish between Pacinian corpuscles, Meissner's corpuscles and pain receptors in the skin.

   Ans: Pacinian corpuscles are located deep in the dermis and in the hypodermis. They function to receive the sensation of deep pressure. Meissner's corpuscles are located just underneath the epidermis and function to perceive light touch. Pain receptors are located in the dermis and respond to numerous pain stimuli.

2. Place labels on the following illustration.

   a. Hair shaft — *b. Epidermis*

   c. Sebaceous gland — *d. Arrector pili*

   e. Hair follicle — *f. Subcutaneous layer*

   g. Hair root — *h. Hair bulb*

3. Hair of the axilla can be considered determinate/indeterminate hair. (Circle the correct answer).

   Ans: determinate

4. Electrolysis is the process of hair removal by using electric current. Explain how this might destroy the process of hair growth in relation to the hair bulb.

   Ans: Electrical 'burning' of the hair bulb destroys the vascular supply to the hair thus preventing growth of the hair.

5. Since hair color is determined by pigment in the cortex and the hair shaft is dead, explain the fallacy of a person's hair turning white overnight.

Ans: Sudden shock may cause a radical change in hair color but that occurs in the hair root. It takes time for the hair to grow out and, as it does, it may turn white. The effects take longer than overnight.

EXERCISE 8
INTRODUCTION TO THE SKELETAL SYSTEM

INTRODUCTION

In this lab the student will be introduced to the nature of bones, the histology of bone, the development of bone and the major bones of the body. There is also a brief description of the cat skeleton in this exercise as well.

The beginning of the exercise covers the major bones of the body. This develops a basic understanding of the skeletal system on which the students can build. The next section covers bone composition. Students can see the demonstration of bones that have been baked, leaving the hydroxyapatite matrix in place while denaturing the proteins. The bones should be brittle and easily broken. These bones can be compared to those that have been soaked in nitric acid or vinegar. Acid dissolves the hydroxyapatite minerals in the bones leaving them pliable but without strength. I use the example of reinforced concrete with the hydroxyapatites represented by the Portland cement for strength and the collagen protein fibers represented by the steel rebar for flexibility.

Another section of the lab covers long bone anatomy with reference to bone growth and development. A discussion of the lengthening of bone via the epiphyseal plate is beneficial and the difference between increase in length and increase in diameter of long bone is also of value. This can be further explored when the student examines decalcified bone and distinguishes between the bone developing osteoblasts and the bone dissolving osteoclasts. In ground bone students should note that the lacunae, which house the bone cells, have been filled with bone dust from the polishing of the bone material.

TIME 2 hours

MATERIALS

Chart of the skeletal system
Cut sections of bone showing compact and spongy bone
Articulated human skeleton
Articulated cat skeleton (if available)
Disarticulated human skeleton (1 per table)
Microscopes
Prepared slides of ground bone
Prepared slides of decalcified bone
Bone heated in oven at 350° F for three hours or more
Bone placed in vinegar for several weeks or 1 N nitric acid for a few days.
Microscopes

REVIEW ANSWERS

1. The hyoid bone belongs to the

   a. appendicular skeleton b. axial skeleton c. upper extremity d. skull

   Ans: b. axial skeleton

2. The clavicle belongs to the

   a. axial skeleton b. pectoral girdle c. pelvic girdle d. upper extremity

   Ans: b. pectoral girdle

3. In the disease osteoporosis there is a significant loss of spongy bone. Explain how the loss of this specific bone material could weaken a bone.

   Ans: Spongy bone has trabeculae which serve as reinforcing struts against a force. The loss of spongy bone causes weakening of the internal support that the compact bone requires and the entire bone breaks.

4. Label the following illustration.

   a. Osteon *b. Canaliculi*

   c. Central canal *d. Lacuna for osteocyte*

   e. Lamella

5. The ends of a long bone are known as the ____________________.

   Ans: epiphyses

6. A carpal bone is classified as a ___________ bone in terms of shape.

   Ans: short

EXERCISE 9
APPENDICULAR SKELETON

INTRODUCTION

For most students, the appendicular skeleton is easier to study than the skull. I have included it before the exercises of the axial skeleton. If students have not seen the major bones of the skeleton they should review Exercise 8 before beginning this section. It is convenient to group the bones according to location, such as the bones of the pectoral girdle, the upper extremity bones, the bones of the pelvic girdle and the lower extremity bones.

The bones of the pectoral girdle are easy to begin with as they are represented only by the scapula and the clavicle. The carpal bones frequently give students difficulty yet if they are grouped in two rows of four they are easier to learn. The groupings are the scaphoid, lunate, triquetral and pisiform and the trapezium, trapezoid, capitate and hamate.

Sometimes students spend more time with the bones if they draw the bones or learn which side of the body they come from. Students typically want to rush through the material and techniques that get them to take a little more time with the material are beneficial. Some instructors tie the learning of the bones to the learning of the muscles. When students learn the bones they are associating them with the origins or insertions of the muscles.

The pelvic girdle bones and the lower extremity bones present little problem though students often want to consider the lateral (third) cuneiform bone as a lateral bone of the foot as opposed to it being the lateral-most of the cuneiform bones. The cuboid is lateral to the lateral cuneiform.

TIME 2 hours

MATERIALS

Articulated skeleton or plastic cast of articulated skeleton
Disarticulated skeleton or plastic casts of bones (1 per table)
Charts of the skeletal system
Plastic drinking straws cut on a bias or pipe cleaners for pointer tips
Foam pads of various sizes (to protect real bones from hard countertops)

REVIEW ANSWERS

1. Label the parts of the scapula in the following illustration

a. Coracoid process — *b. Acromion*

c. Spine — *d. Supraspinous fossa*

e. Infraspinous fossa — *f. Inferior angle*

g. Medial (vertebral) border — *h. Lateral (axillary) border*

2. Label the parts of the ulna as illustrated and determine if the bone is from the left or right side of the body.

a. Olecranon process

b. Trochlear notch

c. Coronoid process

d. Styloid process

e. Head

left ulna

3. A wedding band is typically placed on what phalanx of what digit?

Ans: The band is placed on the proximal phalanx of the fourth digit.

4. Label the following illustration of the foot.

a. Navicular

b. Talus

c. First (medial) Cuneiform

d. Calcaneus

e. Cuboid

f. Third (lateral) Cuneiform

g. Second (intermediate) cuneiform

5. Label the following illustration.

a. Lunate

b. Scaphoid

c. Capitate

d. Hamate

e. Pisiform

f. Triquetrum (triangular)

g. Trapezium

h. Trapezoid

6. On the preceding illustration place an "X" on the proximal phalanx of the fourth digit and a "Y" on the middle phalanx of the second digit. Write a "Z" on the distal phalanx of the first digit.

EXERCISE 10
AXIAL SKELETON—VERTEBRAE, RIBS, STERNUM, HYOID

INTRODUCTION

This exercise covers the axial skeleton exclusive of the skull. The features of a standard or "typical" vertebrae give some students problems as they need to orient the vertebra to the vertebral column and understand the relationship between the pedicle and the lamina of the vertebral arch. Another problem concerns the bifid spinous processes of the cervical vertebrae. It is true that bifid spinous processes occur on the cervical vertebrae but not all of the cervical vertebrae have bifid spinous processes. The cervical vertebrae can be told from the other vertebrae by the presence of the transverse foramina.

The thoracic vertebrae are noted for their rib facets or rib demifacets and the lumbar vertebrae are distinguished by having neither transverse foramina nor rib facets. The sacrum and coccyx are easily recognizable and most students have little problem with the various features of these bones.

The inferior edge of the rib is sharper than the superior edge and along the inferior edge of the rib is the costal groove. Students need to pay attention to distinguishing the head from the tubercle and often it is good to hold a rib next to an articulated skeleton to locate the angle of the rib. It is important to discuss that both males and female have twelve pair of ribs as some students have heard to the contrary. The hyoid is an easy bone to learn with 'cornu' meaning horn.

TIME 2 hours

MATERIALS

Articulated skeleton or plastic cast of skeleton

Disarticulated skeleton or plastic cast of bones (1 per table)

Charts of skeletal system

Plastic drinking straws cut on a bias or pipe cleaners for pointer tips

Foam pads of various sizes (to protect bone from hard countertops)

REVIEW ANSWERS

1. Label the following illustration with the appropriate terms

a. Body *b. Pedicle*

c. Lamina *d. Vertebral arch*

e. Transverse process *f. Spinous process*

2. What part of a rib articulates with the transverse process of a vertebra?

Ans: The tubercle of a rib articulates with the transverse process of a vertebra. The head of the rib articulates with the body of the vertebra.

3. The most inferior portion of the sternum is the

a. body b. manubrium c. angle d. xiphoid

Ans: d. xiphoid

4. Distinguish between the posterior sacral foramina and the sacral canal.

   Ans: The posterior sacral foramina are the holes on either side of the medial sacral crest. The sacral canal is perpendicular to the sacral foramina and is a continuation of the vertebral canal.

5. What 2 features do cervical vertebrae have that no other vertebrae have?

   Ans: Cervical vertebral have transverse foramina and some have a bifid spinous process.

6. Determine from what part of the spinal column the vertebra in the following illustration come.

   Ans: Thoracic

EXERCISE 11
AXIAL SKELETON—SKULL

INTRODUCTION

I like to leave the skull to the last part of the study of the skeletal system due to its complexity. Students should have an introduction to the skull in exercise 8 and if they have not done that exercise they should review the material before beginning this lab. It sometimes helps to have students study the skull by view (lateral, inferior, etc.) and try to see how many skull features are visible from each view. The lab has been oriented by this method though you can have students group the features by individual bones as well.

The ethmoid bone and the sphenoid bone tend to present particular troubles for the beginning anatomy student. Students have a very difficult time orienting the bones to the skull and a disarticulated or Beauchene skull can be of great assistance in aiding your students in placing the sphenoid and ethmoid bones. If you have a skull that has been cut in a midsagittal section the three nasal conchae can easily be seen. The inferior nasal conchae is best discussed as a separate bone while the middle and superior nasal conchae are part of the ethmoid bone.

The term sphenoid comes from the Greek word meaning 'wedge-like' and it 'wedges' in the skull across the width of the skull. The term ethmoid comes from the Greek word meaning 'sieve' and it looks like Swiss cheese with the ethmoid air cells or sinuses passing throughout the bone.

The study of the skull often presents students with problems and if they can study the bones in smaller groups or views they tend to be more successful than trying to learn all of the features of the skull at one time as they study on their own. Most of the skull features can be grouped according to the bone in which they occur.

TIME 2 hours

MATERIALS

Disarticulated skull, if available
Articulated skulls with the calavaria cut
Foam pads to cushion skulls from the desktop
Fetal skulls
Pipe cleaners

REVIEW ANSWERS

1. The mastoid process is located on which bone?

   Ans: Temporal

2. The sagittal suture separates the ________ from the _________.

a. sphenoid, ethmoid

b. left parietal, right parietal

c. frontal, parietal

d. parietals, occipital

Ans: b. left parietal .... right parietal

3. Which bone does <u>not</u> occur in the orbit?

a. maxilla b. zygomatic c. ethmoid d. sphenoid e. temporal

Ans: e. The temporal bone does not comprise part of the orbit.

4. Which bone is <u>not</u> a paired bone of the skull.

a. zygomatic b. temporal c. lacrimal d. vomer

Ans: d. The vomer is not a paired bone of the skull.

5. Label the following illustration.

a. Palatine

b. Maxilla

c. Vomer

d. Zygomatic

e. Occipital

f. Carotid canal

g. Occipital condyles

h. Temporal

i. Mastoid

j. Jugular foramen

6. Label the following illustration.

a. Coronoid process

b. Mandibular notch

c. Condyloid process

d. Ramus

e. Angle

f. Body

g. Mental foramen

EXERCISE 12
ARTICULATIONS

INTRODUCTION

The topic of articulations can be studied in lab by examining the way that bones fit together in an articulated skeleton. Students usually have a keen interest in arthrology as articulations often give people problems from strained joints to arthritis or even joint replacement. By having students examine models of joints such as those of the shoulder or knee and by examining the bony fit of a joint as well as the fresh mammal joint, the study of articulations becomes more accessible.

The dissection of a mammal joint is very important in that students can see the articular cartilage and feel the slippery synovial fluid of the joint. Care should be taken when handling a fresh mammal joint and students should wear gloves or wash their hands thoroughly after handling the specimen. An interesting aspect of the dissection of the mammal joint is to have the students cut into the articular cartilage at the ends of the bone so that they see the nature of this cartilage.

TIME 1 hour

MATERIALS

Mammal joint with intact synovial capsule

Dissection tray with scalpel or razor blades, blunt probe, protective gloves

Waste container with biohazard bag inside

Model or chart of joints including those of the shoulder, knee, hip and jaw

Microscope slides of small mammal joint

Articulated skeleton

REVIEW ANSWERS

1. Which one of the following joints has the greatest range of movement?

   a. gomphosis b. suture c. synchondrosis d. hinge

   Ans: d. hinge

2. In which of these joints would you find a meniscus?

   a. cartilaginous b. fibrous c. synovial

   Ans: c. synovial

3. Label the following illustration.

   a. Joint capsule *b. Synovial membrane*

   c. Bone *d. Articular cartilage*

   e. Synovial cavity

4. Match the joint in the left column with the type of joint in the right column.

__*b*__ acetabulofemoral	a. hinge
__*d*__ radiocarpal	b. ball-and-socket
__*a*__ temporomandibular	c. gliding
__*c*__ vertebrocostal	d. condyloid

5. Rank the following joints in terms of least movable to most movable, with 1 being the least movable and 5 being the most movable.

Ans:

gliding	*3*
saddle	*4*
suture	*1*
syndesmosis	*2*
ball-and-socket	*5*

6. What is the function of the meniscus in the knee?

Ans: To provide cushioning, preventing the femur from hitting the tibia.

7. What is the function of the labrum in the glenohumeral joint?

Ans: The labrum functions to increase the depth of the glenoid fossa providing greater stability to the joint.

EXERCISES 13–18
GENERAL IDEAS FOR THE STUDY OF HUMAN AND CAT MUSCULATURE

There seem to be two main groups of students—those that love the study of muscle anatomy and those that do not. Some students who do not normally excel in other areas of anatomy identify with the study of the muscles and consider this section the highlight of the course. Others seem to understand the importance of the study of muscles but do not like to focus on the details of the particular origins, insertions, actions and innervations of the muscles.

Frequently the use of an articulated skeleton helps students locate the muscle origins and insertions and from that point the actions become more comprehensible. Often the use of a string placed between the origin and insertion of a muscle helps students understand the action, particularly if they can see what would happen if the string shortens.

You may wish to customize the muscle list and have students learn specific muscles or specific things about each muscle. Some students will pick up on muscles quickly and be able to learn them easily. Other students may have to draw each muscle separately to identify where that muscle originates and inserts. If students can locate the muscle on themselves they can often learn the material easier. The visualization of the muscle is crucial to learning where it occurs and what it does. Muscles in these exercises are grouped by where they originate, insert or by the nature of their action.

EXERCISE 13
INTRODUCTION TO THE STUDY OF MUSCLES AND MUSCLES OF THE SHOULDER AND ARM

INTRODUCTION

The very beginning muscle lab presents a challenge to beginning students. If you are dissecting cats as study specimens you may want to spend an entire lab period removing the skin and removing the superficial fascia from the muscles. There is great sensitivity among members of the general population as to the dissection of animals or use of animals in science. Ignoring concerns of students or community members may be an invitation to serious altercations and a good degree of advanced diplomacy may be in order, on your part, so that students understand the benefit of animal dissection in their studies.

In this exercise students will learn the superficial muscles of the shoulder and arm (or forearm) in humans and cats. It is very important to emphasize the human musculature in the exercise and the use of cats as surrogate species. Some students get careless with the use of scalpels and need to be reminded that these instruments are potentially dangerous.

Students should be directed to proper clean-up procedures and keep dissection remains out of sink drains and into appropriate containers for disposal. Frequently the local animal shelter will dispose of animal remains for a fee.

TIME 2-3 hours to skin the cat, 2 hours for muscle study

MATERIALS

Human torso model
Human arm models
Human muscle charts
Articulated skeleton
Cadaver (if available)
Cat (if available) (1 per pair of students)
Cat wetting solution
Materials for cat dissection
- Dissection trays
- Scalpel and two to three extra blades
- Gloves (household latex gloves work well for repeated use)
- Blunt (Mall) probe
- String and tags
- Pins
- Forceps and sharp scissors

First aid kit in lab or prep area
Sharps container
Animal waste disposal container

REVIEW ANSWERS

1. In terms of human muscles:

a. What is the action of the deltoid muscle?

Ans: Abducts arm, flexes, extends, medially and laterally rotates arm

b. Name the origin of the supraspinatus muscle.

Ans: Supraspinous fossa

c. What is the insertion of the trapezius muscle?

Ans: Clavicle, spine and acromion process of scapula

d. Does the biceps brachii muscle originate or insert on the humerus?

Ans: No.

e. What is the insertion of the pectoralis minor?

Ans: Coracoid process of scapula

2. In terms of cat muscles:

a. What is the action of the epitrochlearis?

Ans: Extension of the forelimb

b. Circle the muscle that does <u>not</u> correspond to a human muscle: biceps brachii, brachialis, xiphihumeralis, latissimus dorsi

Ans: xiphihumeralis

c. How does the deltoid of the cat differ from the deltoid of the human?

Ans: The deltoid in cats is actually three muscles the clavodeltoid, the acromiodeltoid and the spinodeltoid.

3. Match each term on the left with a description on the right.

d. dissect	a. what a muscle does
e. flexion	b. to cut a muscle in half
f. reflect	c. to stabilize a joint
b. transect	d. to separate muscles
a. action	e. to decrease a joint angle
c. fixing	f. to pull back a muscle

EXERCISE 14
MUSCLES OF THE FOREARM AND HAND

INTRODUCTION

The forearm and hand muscles are more challenging to study due to their similarity in appearance. It is very beneficial to learn the origins and insertions of the muscles at the same time as the location of the muscle. The muscles that flex the forearm generally have origins on or near the medial epicondyle of the humerus. The term *carpi* refers to an insertion on the carpals or metacarpals. The term *radialis* or *ulnaris* refers to the lateral or medial side of the hand respectively. The term *digitorum* refers to an insertion on the digits 2-5 (the index finger to the little finger) while the term *pollicis* refers to an insertion on the thumb. The extensor muscles have a common origin on the lateral epicondyle of the humerus and are fewer in number than the flexor group.

The superficial muscles of the anterior forearm in the humans are the brachioradialis, the flexor carpi radialis, the pronator teres, the palmaris longus and the flexor carpi ulnaris.

The flexor digitorum superficialis is the superficial digit flexor (as opposed to the deep digit flexor) and it is <u>not</u> a superficial forearm muscle. It is located deep to the palmaris longus and the flexor carpi radialis. The flexor digitorum superficialis is superficial to the flexor digitorum profundus, the latter of which originates on the ulna.

The muscle that extends most of the digits of the hand is the extensor digitorum communis. It serves to open the hand. Numerous muscles have and action on the thumb and these muscles provide for the versatility of motion of the thumb.

TIME 2-3 hours

MATERIALS

Human torso model
Human arm models
Human muscle charts
Articulated skeleton
Cadaver (if available)
Cat (if available)
Materials for cat dissection (1 per student or pair of students)
- Dissection trays and equipment
- Gloves
- String

REVIEW ANSWERS

1. What is the origin of the flexor carpi ulnaris in humans?

   Ans: Medial epicondyle of the humerus, olecranon process, and dorsal border of the ulna.

2. What is an antagonist to the supinator muscle?

   Ans: Pronator teres or pronator quadratus

3. Where does the flexor digitorum superficialis of the human insert?

    Ans: Middle phalanges of second through fifth digits

4. What is the insertion of the extensor carpi ulnaris muscle?

    Ans: Metacarpal 5

5. Which muscle is more developed in cats, the flexor digitorum superficialis or the flexor digitorum profundus?

    Ans: Flexor digitorum profundus

EXERCISE 15
MUSCLES OF THE HIP AND THIGH

INTRODUCTION

This group of muscles is relatively easy to study as they are either familiar to most (gluteus maximus, quadriceps, hamstrings) or are more distinct than the muscles of the forearm and hand. Some of these muscles have more of an importance in maintaining balance (such as the gluteus medius and gluteus minimus) than they do for their stated action (abduction of the thigh). As the swing foot comes forward these muscles on the opposite side maintain the center of gravity.

Likewise the gluteus maximus is more important in standing up or climbing stairs than it is in walking. The hamstrings are very important in extension of the thigh in walking. The muscles of the hip and thigh can be grouped together for ease of learning. For example, all of the muscles grouped as the quadriceps femoris muscles extend the leg. All of the hamstring muscles share a common origin (the ischial tuberosity) and have the same action (extend the thigh and flex the leg).

TIME 2-3 hours

MATERIALS

Human torso model
Human leg models
Human muscle charts
Articulated skeleton
Cadaver (if available)
Cat (if available)
Materials for cat dissection (1 per student or pair of students)

- Dissection trays
- Scalpel or razor blades
- Gloves
- Blunt probe
- String
- Pins

REVIEW ANSWERS

1. If you were to ride a horse, what muscles would you use to keep your seat out of the saddle as you ride?

   Ans: Adductor muscles

2. How does the gluteus medius and gluteus minimus prevent you from toppling over as you walk?

   Ans: They work by pulling the top of the ilium and the lateral surface of the femur closer together on the stance leg. As the swing leg is in motion the center of gravity of the body tends to move in the direction of the swing leg. The gluteus medius and gluteus minimus prevent this motion.

3. What is a muscle that is an antagonist to the biceps femoris muscle?

   Ans: The rectus femoris. The biceps femoris extends the thigh and flexes the leg while the rectus femoris flexes the thigh and extends the leg.

4. What are two muscles that are synergists with the biceps femoris muscle?

   Ans: The semitendinosus and the semimembranosus

5. Are all of the hamstring muscles identical in action? What is the action of the hamstring muscles?

   Ans: Yes, the actions of the hamstrings are identical. They serve to extend the thigh and flex the leg.

6. What is the insertion of all the muscles of the quadriceps group?

   Ans: The insertion of the quadriceps group is the tibial tuberosity by the patellar tendon.

7. How does the action of the rectus femoris differ from all the other quadriceps muscles?

   Ans: The rectus femoris, in addition to extending the leg as do all the quadriceps muscles also flexes the thigh.

EXERCISE 16
MUSCLES OF THE LEG AND FOOT

INTRODUCTION

The muscles of the leg and foot can be studied with the muscles of the hip and thigh or as a separate lab exercise. The gastrocnemius and soleus are major muscles of the posterior surface while the tibialis anterior and the extensor digitorum longus are major muscles on the anterior surface of the leg.

The peroneus longus and brevis function to plantar flex the foot because the tendons of these muscles hook behind the lateral malleolus of the fibula. The peroneus tertius does not loop behind the lateral malleolus and thus dorsiflexes the foot.

TIME 2-3 hours

MATERIALS

Human torso model
Human leg models
Human muscle charts
Articulated skeleton
Cadaver (if available)
Cat (if available)
Materials for cat dissection (1 per student or pair of students)
- Dissection trays
- Scalpel or razor blades
- Gloves
- Blunt probe
- String
- Pins

REVIEW ANSWERS

1. What is the origin of the gastrocnemius?

   Ans: Condyles of the femur.

2. What is the insertion of the tibialis anterior in humans?

   Ans: First metatarsal and first cuneiform

3. How does the action of the peroneus longus in humans differ from that of the peroneus tertius?

   Ans: In humans the peroneus longus plantarflexes and everts the foot while the peroneus tertius dorsiflexes and everts the foot.

4. What is the action of the extensor hallucis longus?

   Ans: It extends the hallux (big toe) and dorsiflexes the foot.

5. Fill in the following illustration.

   a. Tibialis anterior *b. Peroneus longus*

   c. Soleus *d. Extensor digitorium longus*

EXERCISE 17
MUSCLES OF THE HEAD AND NECK

INTRODUCTION

The muscles of the head and neck are numerous and have multiple functions. Some of the muscles are involved in moving the head or neck such as the sternocleidomastoid or the scalenus muscles while other muscles are involved in expression such as the risorius or the frontalis muscles. Still other muscles are involved in chewing like the temporalis and the masseter muscles and others are sphincter muscles such as the orbicularis oculi and the orbicularis oris.

The cat differs from the human in that the cat has enlarged masseter muscles compared to the human. Dissection of the head musculature involves skill in handling the scalpel especially in uncovering the delicate muscles of the face.

TIME 2-3 hours

MATERIALS

Human torso model or head and neck model
Human muscle charts
Articulated skeleton
Cadaver (if available)
Cat (if available)
Materials for cat dissection
- Dissection trays
- Scalpel or razor blades
- Gloves
- Blunt probe
- String
- Pins

REVIEW ANSWERS

1. What is the origin of the masseter muscle?

   Ans: Zygomatic arch

2. What is a synergist of the masseter muscle?

   Ans: Temporalis muscle

3. Where is the origin of the levator scapulae muscle?

   Ans: Cervical vertebrae 1-4

4. What kind of muscle is the orbicularis oculi or orbicularis oris muscle in terms of function?

   Ans: They are sphincter muscles.

5. Fill in the following illustration.

   a. Frontalis — *b. Temporalis*
   c. Orbicularis oculi — *d. Masseter*
   e. Orbicularis oris — *f. Buccinator*

EXERCISE 18
MUSCLES OF THE TRUNK

INTRODUCTION

The muscles of the trunk can be divided into the abdominal muscles, the deep back muscles, the respiratory muscles and the muscles of the posterior neck. The abdominal muscles function to compress the abdominal viscera which aids in breathing, having a bowel movement and in vomiting. The deep back muscles are mostly postural muscles as are the deep muscles of the posterior neck. The respiratory muscles are covered in this exercise and they are referred to in the respiratory anatomy lab (Exercise 39). The internal and external intercostals are responsible for thoracic breathing while the diaphragm is important in abdominal breathing.

TIME 2-3 hours

MATERIALS

Human torso model
Human muscle charts
Articulated skeleton
Cadaver (if available)
Cat (if available)
Materials for cat dissection
- Dissection trays
- Scalpel or razor blades
- Gloves
- Blunt probe
- String
- Pins

REVIEW ANSWERS

1. What is the action of the serratus anterior muscle?

   Ans: Abduction of the scapula

2. Which *five* muscles have an action that extends the vertebral column?

   Ans: Spinalis, longissimus, iliocostalis, multifidus, quadratus lumborum (and semispinalis as well)

3. What is the action of the rhomboideus muscles?

   Ans: Adduction of the scapula

4. How does the serratus anterior function as an antagonist to the rhomboideus muscles?

   Ans: The serratus anterior abducts the scapula while the rhomboideus muscles adduct the scapula.

5. How does the action of the rectus abdominis differ from the other abdominal muscles?

   Ans: The rectus abdominis flexes the vertebral column in addition to compressing the abdominal wall. The other abdominal muscles compress the abdominal wall and laterally rotate the trunk.

6. What is the physical relationship of the intercostal muscles to each other?

Ans: The external intercostals are superficial to the internal intercostals. The external intercostals have fibers that run in the same direction as the external oblique muscle when viewed from the front. The internal intercostal muscles are deep to the externals and have fibers that run in the same direction as the internal obliques when viewed from the front.

EXERCISE 19
MUSCLE PHYSIOLOGY

INTRODUCTION

The physiology of muscle contraction can either be demonstrated by the use of frog gastrocnemius muscle as a surrogate for human muscle or a recording of human musculature can be done using conventional physiographs or physio-computers. The resistance by some students to use frogs in experiments can be decreased if the frogs are pithed away from the students' lab tables (such as pithing them in the prep area ahead of time) and if a proper introduction is given as to the value of using experimental animals and the importance of the results gained.

This section covers the materials and formulae for preparation of solutions, a brief description of the set-up for a duograph set-up and the set-up for a Biopac module. This lab should be well planned if you have never done it before and you should make sure that the equipment is operational prior to using it in the lab. Frequently the stimuli and recording knobs need to be adjusted for each experiment.

TIME 2 hours

MATERIALS

Large grass frog or bullfrog (1 per experiment)
Frog Ringer's solution in dropper bottles (150 mls per experiment)

Frog Ringer's Solution

6.5 g $NaCl$ (sodium chloride)
0.2 g $NaHCO_3$ (sodium bicarbonate)
0.1 g $CaCl_2$ (calcium chloride)
0.1 g KCl (potassium chloride)
Add enough water to make 1000 ml
Thread
Duograph, physiograph or computer
Myograph transducer
Stimulator and cables
Scissors
Clean, live animal dissection pan
Sharp pithing probes
Glass hooks
Scalpel
Pins

Set-up

There are numerous set-up procedures for the registration of frog gastrocnemius muscle contraction. One method using a Duograph and a Grass stimulator is listed below.

Duograph Set-up

Calibration

1. Plug in the machine and let it warm up
2. Set turn dial to **DC CAL**
3. Set top toggle to **Hi Filter**
4. Set lower toggle to **Norm**
5. Set turn dial to **0.1** mv/cm
6. Set stylus heat control to 2-o'clock position
7. Turn vernier **Trans bal** counterclockwise to zero
8. Press 1mv red button to get deflection on paper
9. Adjust **Sensitivity** and **Centering** knobs to get 1 cm deflection
   (make sure stylus is in center of paper)
10. Set turn dial to **Trans** (Transducer) setting
11. Adjust upper vernier **trans**ducer **bal**ance clockwise to bring pen to
    center of paper
12. Set Step sensitivity to **2 mv/cm** (2 = least sensitive, 0.1 = most sensitive)
13. Turn Standby to Operate
14. Suspend 100g weight from muscle transducer
    You should get 5 cm deflection by adjusting amplifier sensitivity
15. Tie muscle to 2 leaves of transducer

Stimulator Set-up

1. Set polarity to "+"
2. Set output to B1

In recording various physiological events the following guidelines may be of help. Stimulators, myographs and frogs all vary so these are to be used as a general guideline. Adjustments will probably be necessary.

Threshold stimulus

Stimulator

Duration (length of stimulus)—2 msec (10 × 0.2)

Frequency—2 pulses/sec (2 Hz)

Voltage—Zero (0 X 0.1)

Stimulus—repeat stimulus

Duograph

Chart speed = 0.1 cm/sec

Increase voltage by 0.1 volt until perceptible contraction

Treppe

Stimulator

Voltage—10 V

Stimulus 1 Hz (1 pulse/sec)

Note stepwise increase as muscle "warms-up"

Spatial summation (maximum recruitment of fibers)

Stimulator

Duration—2 msec (10 × 0.2)

Frequency—2 pulses/sec (2 Hz)

Voltage—Zero (0 × 0.1)

Stimulus—repeat stimulus

Chart speed = 0.1 cm/sec

Increase voltage until maximum response is reached.

Single twitch

Stimulator

Duration—2 msec (10 × 0.2)

Frequency—2 pulses/sec (2 Hz)

Voltage—Determined by maximum recruitment

Stimulus—repeat stimulus 1 pulse/ 2-3 sec.

Chart speed = 100 mm/sec (max. chart speed)

Tetany

Stimulator

Duration—2 msec (10 × 0.2)

Frequency—4 pulses/sec (4 Hz)

Voltage—Determined by maximum recruitment

Stimulus—repeat stimulus 2/sec

Duograph

Chart speed = 5mm/sec

Increase. Hz from 4 to 8, 10, 12, 14, 16, 18 etc. until smooth curve is obtained.

Alternative labs, that avoid animal dissection, can be set up with Intellitool, Biopac, or other systems. The Biopac procedure is described next.

BIOPAC

Muscle exercises are available that do not involve the sacrifice of live animals. One of the exercises available is the electromyogram (EMG) developed by Biopac. The system requires a personal computer, the four channel hardware unit (MP 30), disposable electrodes and the electrode leads. The red lead is attached near the wrist, the white lead a few centimeters proximal to the elbow and the black lead near the antecubital fossa. The log-on procedures are fairly easy by clicking on the "Start setup" button on the monitor display. You can then record the data by pressing on the "Record 1A" button as described in the "Biopac Student Lab Manual" and either flexing the forearm or by adding successively heavier weights

"Biopac Student Lab Manual" and either flexing the forearm or by adding successively heavier weights to the arm. You can measure the minimum and maximum volts, peak to peak values or record an integrated electromyogram. Material is available from:

Biopac Systems, Inc.
42 Aero Camino
Goleta, CA 93117
(805) 685-0066

REVIEW ANSWERS

1. Define subthreshold stimulus.

   Ans: A subthreshold stimulus is one where the impulse is too low to elicit a response (a muscle contraction).

2. Describe tetany.

   Ans: Tetany is the continuous smooth contraction of muscle brought about by rapid, sequential stimuli.

3. What is maximum recruitment?

   Ans: Maximum recruitment is the stimulus needed to cause all of the muscle fibers to contract.

4. How does tetany and twitch as demonstrated in the lab correlate to human muscle contraction? Which one is more reflective of human muscle response? Why?

   Ans: Human muscles do not normally respond by singular contractions seen as twitches. Human muscle contraction occurs by numerous firings which are demonstrated in lab by tetanic contractions. These tetanic contractions are more reflective of normal human muscular response.

5. In the following illustration, place an "A" on the latent period, a "B" on the contraction phase and a "C" on the relaxation phase.

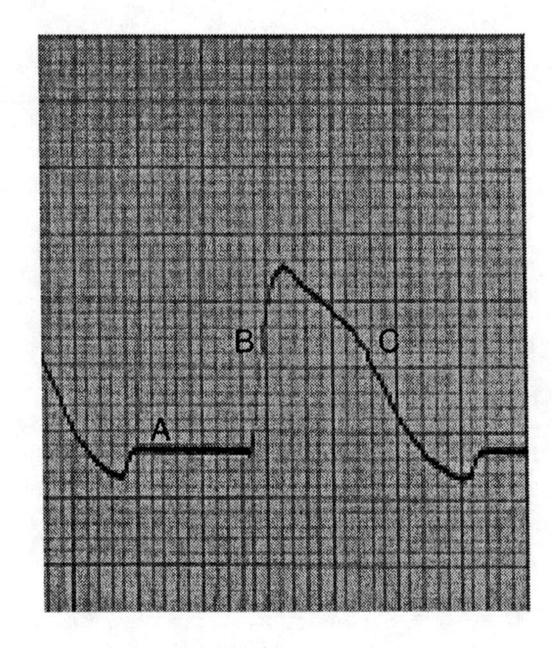

6. What was the threshold stimulus you obtained in lab?

   Ans: Determined by experimentation

7. What was the voltage at which you first got maximum recruitment?

   Ans: Determined by experimentation

8. Explain a muscle spasm in terms of recruitment of muscle fibers.

   Ans: A muscle spasm is the spontaneous recruitment of numerous muscle fibers. The spasmodic contraction of muscle fibers causes painful contractions.

EXERCISE 20
INTRODUCTION TO THE NERVOUS SYSTEM

INTRODUCTION

This exercise involves the introduction to the nervous system and the study of nerve cells. A general introduction to the nature of the nervous system is of value as students can integrate the microscopic anatomy of the system more effectively if the overview is in place. Descriptions of sensory and motor pathways are covered here as an introduction and revisited in the exercise on reflexes (Exercise 23).

Drawings of neuron shapes are often beneficial for beginning students and good illustrative material covering the neurons and neuroglia is also beneficial. The particular structure of Schwann cells and saltatory conduction is important here.

TIME 2 hours

MATERIALS

Charts or models of the nervous system
Charts or models of neurons
Microscopes
Prepared slides of:
- Spinal cord smear
- Longitudinal section of nerve
- Neuroglia (if available)
- Cerebrum
- Cerebellum

REVIEW ANSWERS

1. Draw a neuron in the space provided and label the axon, dendrite, and nerve cell body along with the Nissl bodies and axon hillock.

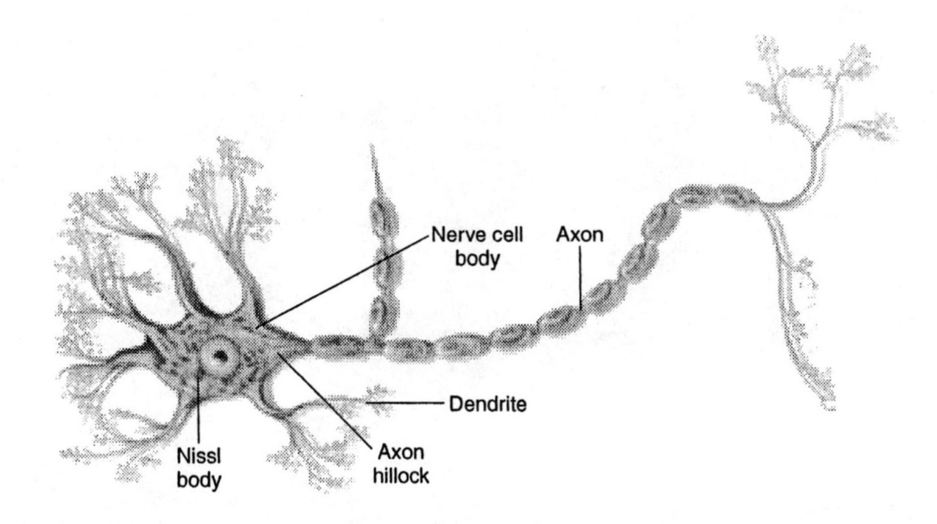

2. Draw a pseudounipolar neuron and label the parts.

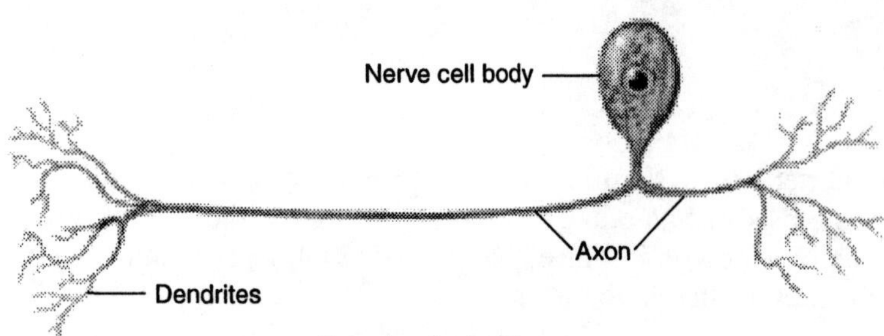

Pseudounipolar Neuron

3. Describe the function of:

a. an astrocyte:

Ans: Along with the capillaries they provide the barrier between the blood and the brain. They protect the brain from some potential pathogens found in the blood.

b. an ependymal cell:

Ans: These cells line cavities and provide a barrier between the nervous tissue and the cerebrospinal fluid.

c. an oligodendrocyte:

Ans: They serve to produce myelin in the CNS. This speeds up neural firing.

4. The brain belongs to what division of the nervous system?

Ans: Central nervous system

5. A spinal nerve belongs to what division of the nervous system?

Ans: Peripheral nervous system

EXERCISE 21
STRUCTURE AND FUNCTION OF THE BRAIN AND CRANIAL NERVES

INTRODUCTION

This laboratory exercise is a brief introduction to the study of the brain. I find it beneficial for students to examine models and charts in lab prior to looking at preserved specimens. Sheep brains are commonly used as dissection specimens though they differ somewhat from prosected human brains. The pons is smaller in sheep brains and the corpora quadrigemina is larger. Sheep, being quadrupeds, have the medulla oblongata in line with the long axis of the brain. In humans the medulla oblongata is at a ninety degree angle to the long axis of the brain.

It is important that students know the structure of the brain prior to learning the cranial nerves. If students can associate the cranial nerves with the anatomy of the brain the nerves will be easier to find. If you provide clues to the location of the cranial nerves students will learn the nerves more effectively. Information such as the location of the trigeminal nerve being at ninety degrees to the long axis to the pons helps students distinguish this nerve from the others.

As with the skull descriptions, I have written the lab so that students examine the brain from various views. Another method to learning the brain is to study all of the structures of the cerebrum, diencephalon, mesencephalon or rhombencephalon and examine each of these regions from different views.

TIME 2-3 hours

MATERIALS

Models and charts of the human brain
Preserved human brains (if available)
Cast of the ventricles of the brain
Chart, section, or illustration of the brain in coronal and transverse sections
Sheep brains
Dissection trays
Scalpels or razor blades
Gloves
Blunt probes

REVIEW ANSWERS

1. John pulled a 'no-brainer' by hitting his forehead against the wall. What possible damage might he do to the function of his brain, particularly those functions associated with the frontal lobe?

   Ans: The damage done may be to the brain, the meninges or both. A concussion is a "brain bruise" and the functions of the frontal lobe such as intelligence and creativity might be impaired.

2. If a stroke affected all of the sensations interpreted by the brain just concerning the face and the hands, how much of the postcentral gyrus would be affected?

   Approximately one half of the post-central gyrus would be affected.

3. Approximately 91% of people are right handed, and the description of cerebral hemispheres is appropriate for them. In left-handed individuals the pattern is typically reversed. One convenient excuse that people often make for their inability to do something is to describe themselves as left-brained or right-brained individuals. Describe what effect the loss of an entire cerebral hemisphere would have on specific functions such as spatial awareness or the ability to speak.

   Ans: The motor speech area is normally found only on the left side of the brain. Damage to this area can cause permanent speech impairment in that thoughts cannot be articulated as fluent speech.

4. Aphasia is loss of speech. There are different types of aphasia that can occur. If Broca's area was affected by a stroke, would the content of the spoken word be affected or would the ability to pronounce the words be affected?

   Ans: The ability to pronounce words would be affected.

5. Label the following illustration using the terms provided.

   a. Corpus callosum *b. Mesencephalic aqueduct* *c. Pons*

   d. Pineal gland *e. Thalamus* *f. Arbor vitae*

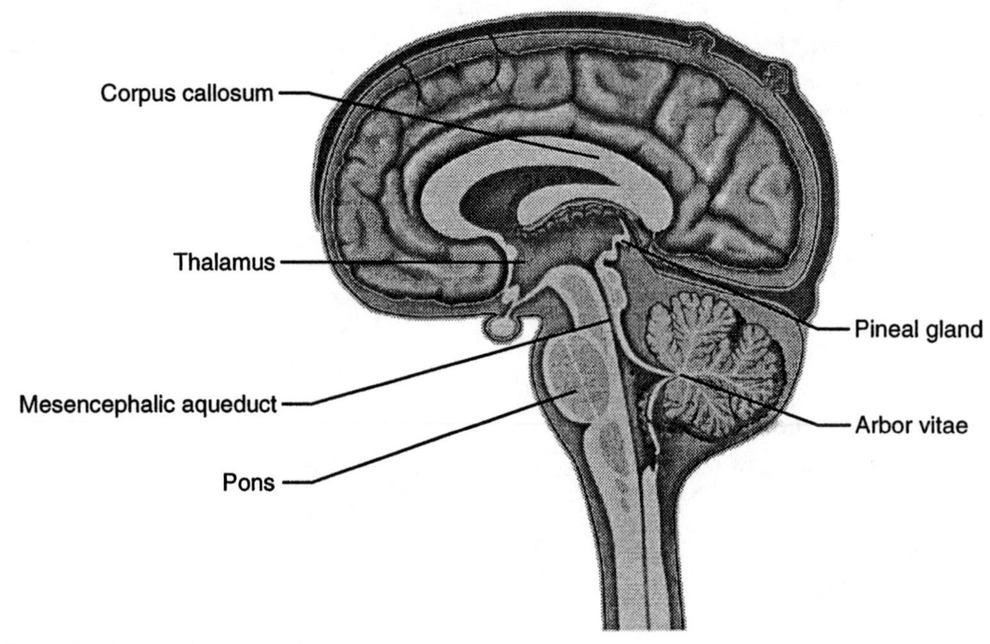

6. Label the following illustration using the terms provided.

   a. Olfactory bulb *b. Trigeminal nerve* *c. Vagus nerve*

   d. Facial nerve *e. Medulla oblongata* *f. Pons*

EXERCISE 22
STRUCTURE AND FUNCTION OF THE SPINAL CORD AND NERVES

INTRODUCTION

After having studied many histological specimens under high power, students often want to examine the spinal cord using the high, dry objective. Ask students to place the prepared slide of a cross section of spinal cord on a piece of white paper and look at it with no magnification. You can also have them place the slide under a dissecting microscope to examine the general features.

TIME 1.5 hours

MATERIALS

Models or charts of the central and peripheral nervous systems
Prepared slide of a spinal cord in cross section
Model or chart of a spinal cord in cross section and longitudinal section

REVIEW ANSWERS

1. What type of impulse (sensory/motor) travels through the

   a. anterior gray horn?

   Ans: motor

   b. posterior gray horn?

   Ans: sensory

   c. ascending spinal tracts?

   Ans: sensory

   d. descending spinal tracts?

   Ans: motor

2. What major nerves arise from the following plexuses?

   a. cervical

   Ans: Phrenic nerve

   b. brachial

   Ans: Musculocutaneous, axillary, radial, median, and ulnar nerves

   c. lumbar

   Ans: Femoral nerve

   d. sacral

   Ans: Sciatic nerve

3. How does the dorsal spinal root vary from the ventral spinal root?

Ans: The dorsal spinal root carries sensory impulses to the spinal cord and the ventral spinal root carries motor impulses from the spinal cord.

4. What causes the cervical enlargement of the spinal cord?

Ans: The cervical enlargement is due to increased neural information coming from and going to the upper extremities.

EXERCISE 23
NERVOUS SYSTEM PHYSIOLOGY - STIMULI AND REFLEXES

INTRODUCTION

Students have varying sensitivities to the dissection of live animals for experimental purposes. A small discussion prior to conducting the experiment is often helpful so that students are aware of the value of animals in experimentation and your willingness to be open to individual concerns.

Nerves should normally respond to almost any significant stimulus. However nerves treated with procaine hydrochloride should not respond.

Students generally enjoy the reflex portion of the exercise. Responses to environmental stimuli (such as the patellar reflex) may be reduced if the student has thick patellar tendons. The results from the reflex portion of the lab should not be considered clinically relevant though a student with significant hyporeflexia or hyperreflexia may wish to consult a physician.

TIME 2-3 hours

MATERIALS

Nerve physiology section

Frog (1 per pair of students)
Latex or plastic gloves (1 box each of small, medium and large gloves)
Glass rod with hook at one end (1 per pair of students)
Hot pad or mitt (1 per pair of students)
Bunsen burner (1 per pair of students)
Matches or flint lighter (1 per pair of students)
Frog Ringer's solution in dropper bottles (1 per pair of students)

Frog Ringer's Solution

6.5 g NaCl	(sodium chloride)
0.2 g $NaHCO_3$	(sodium bicarbonate)
0.1 g $CaCl_2$	(calcium chloride)
0.1 g KCl	(potassium chloride)

Add enough water to make 1000 ml
Microscope slide or small glass plate (1 per pair of students)
Filter paper or paper towel (1 per pair of students)
Dissection equipment for live animals (1 per pair of students)
Scalpel or scissors (1 per pair of students)
Cotton sewing thread (1 per pair of students)
Stimulator apparatus with probe (1 per pair of students)

5% sodium chloride solution (1 dropper bottle per table)

0.1% hydrochloric acid solution (1 ml of concentrated HCl in 1 liter of water)

Procaine hydrochloride solution (1 bottle at instructor's table)

(1 g of Procaine Hydrochloride dissolves in 1 ml H_2O and 30 ml ROH)

Reflex section

Patellar reflex hammer (1 per pair of students)

Rubber squeeze bulb (1 per pair of students)

Models or charts of spinal cord and nerves

REVIEW ANSWERS

1. After patients leave the operating room they are transferred to an area called the "recovery room." Correlate the meaning of the word "recovery" in this context with what you have learned about the recovery of nerves in this exercise.

   Ans: The anesthetics inhibit the neuronal firing in local and general anesthesia. The recovery room is a place where patients allow their neurons to recover from the effects of general anesthetics.

2. Draw a monosynaptic reflex arc in the space provided. Label your illustration with the terms provided.

Stimulus

Motor neuron

Effector

Sensory neuron

Synapse

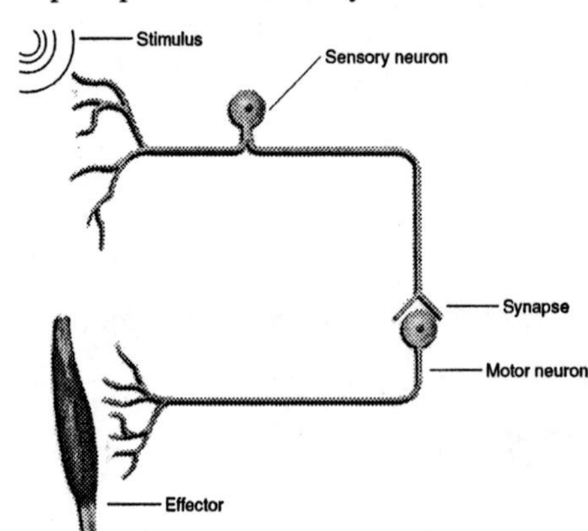

3. What action occurs with a hyperreflexic response? What action happens with a hyporeflexic response?

   Ans: In a hyperreflexic response the individual has exaggerated responses to the stimuli. In a hyporeflexic response the individual does not respond very much to the stimulus.

4. List the positive responses obtained in the frog experiment and correlate this with the specificity of neuronal sensitivity.

   Ans: Determined by experimentation

5. What was the threshold voltage observed in the nerve response?

   Ans: Determined by experimentation

EXERCISE 24
INTRODUCTION TO SENSORY ORGANS

INTRODUCTION

This is the first of four labs concerning sense organs. Most of this lab covers integumentary functions involving touch, temperature, adaptation and referred pain. In the two-point discrimination test, students should vary the distance between the discriminator points to validate their lab partner's response. There are some experiments that have more than one variable. In the test of adaptation to touch, the ability to sense the slow withdrawal of a hand from the arm is one variable and the ability to move the hand away slowly, so that the change is not well perceived, is another variable. Likewise the experiment on locating a stimulus with proprioception has a variable in determining where the first mark was felt and the second variable of being able to physically locate that mark while the eyes are closed. Even with two variables the experiments offer a valuable insight to the functions of the sense organs.

TIME 1.5 hours

MATERIALS

Blunt metal probes (2 per student pair)

Dishpan of ice water or large finger bowls (2 L)

Dishpan of room temperature water

Dishpan of warm water (45° C)

Towels (6 per lab)

Small centimeter ruler (1 per student pair)

Black, fine-tipped felt markers (1 per student pair)

Red, fine-tipped felt markers (1 per student pair)

Blue, fine-tipped felt markers (1 per student pair)

Two-point discriminators (or a mechanical compass) (1 per student pair)

Von Frey hairs (1 per student pair)

REVIEW ANSWERS

1. An area with a great number of nerve endings is the upper lip. What can you predict about the ability of the upper lip to distinguish two points?

   Ans: Due to the number of nerve endings, the upper lip is very good at distinguishing between two points.

2. When you extend the temperature beyond the level of cool and warm, the pain receptors in the skin are activated. Cool receptors are activated between 12° and 35° C. Warm receptors are activated between 25° and 35° C. You or your lab partner may have had an experience with very cold conditions such as when cleaning out a freezer or holding dry ice. What perception is sensed?

   Ans: When extremely cold material comes into contact with the skin the pain receptors are stimulated and often this is interpreted as a hot sensation. The 'burning' seems odd when the person is holding something known to be cold.

3. Adaptation is very important to sensory stimulation. We are bombarded with stimuli during most of the day, and much of what we sense is filtered from conscious thought. The sense of touch experiences adaptation, yet pain usually does not adapt. How is the sense of adaptation to touch used by pickpockets?

   Ans: Pickpockets rely on the sense of adaptation in that if they can deftly remove a wallet the sensation of the wallet continues to be perceived even though the object is no longer there. Frequently a pickpocket will try to have the intended victim focus on another perception (such as a tap on the shoulder) as the wallet is being lifted.

4. In terms of receptor density, describe why it is difficult to find the same location on the forearm when your eyes are closed?

   Ans: There are two variables in this exercise. One is the ability to perceive a location and the other is to touch that location. In areas where receptors are in close proximity (such as on the tip of the finger) the ability to discriminate between two points is easily done. In areas where the touch receptors are more widely scattered (as on the arm or forearm) the perception is more difficult to locate.

EXERCISE 25
TASTE AND SMELL

INTRODUCTION

The chemoreceptors that perceive taste and smell are so closely linked that it is reasonable to cover them together. As this is a lab where students are ingesting material it is important to make sure that there is a one-way flow from the stock solutions, to the student, and then to the waste container.

Students vary in their sensitivity to taste with some students strongly objecting to acid or bitter tastes. Some students may be hypersensitive to the dilute perfume. Ask, in advance, if any student is sensitive to perfumes or has food allergies to the fruit nectars in lab. If so, advise the student to be the recorder for that part of the experiment.

TIME 1.5 hours

MATERIALS

Cotton-tipped applicators (4 per student)
Disposable (paper) cups 4-12 oz cups containing one of the following:
- Solution of salt water (3%)
- Quinine solution (0.5% quinine sulfate)
- Vinegar solution (household vinegar or 5% acetic acid solution)
- Sugar solution (3% sucrose)

Biohazard bag
Prepared slides of taste buds
Microscopes
Roll of household paper towels
Small bowl of salt crystals (household salt)
Small bowl of sugar crystals (household granulated sugar)
Flat toothpicks (1 box per lab)
Several small vials (10-20 ml) screw-cap bottles with cotton saturated with essential oil labeled "Peppermint", "Almond", "Wintergreen" and "Camphor" (keep vials in separate wide-mouthed jars to prevent cross-contamination of scent).
Four small vials colored red and labeled "Wild Cherry" filled with benzaldehyde solution. Benzaldehyde is imitation almond extract. You can use pure almond extract (e.g. Schilling ®) from the supermarket.
One vial of dilute perfume (1 part perfume, 5 parts ethyl alcohol)
Selection of 4 or 5 fruit nectars (such as Kern's nectars), 2 cans each per lab: apricot, coconut/pineapple, strawberry, mango, peach
Small, 3 oz paper cups (89 ml) [5 per student (or student pair)]
Napkins

REVIEW ANSWERS

1. Can you determine the adaptation for having taste buds that determine unpleasant bitter compounds in many plant species?

   Ans: The adaptation is valuable in that bitter compounds frequently are poisons in plants.

2. Some individuals with severe sinus infections can lose their senses of smell. How could an infection that spreads from the frontal or maxillary sinus impair the sense of smell?

   Ans: An infection in the frontal or maxillary sinus could spread to the ethmoid bone which houses the olfactory nerves. If these nerves were damaged severely then the sense of smell could be permanently affected.

3. Material must be in solution for it to be tasted. What process would be used (olfaction, gustation) to perceive a lipid-based food?

   Ans: Olfaction. There are four sensations of taste which are sensitive to water soluble materials. Lipid-based materials such as mint oil, garlic oil are sensed by smell.

4. Some smells that we perceive as two separate smells are actually identical. What are the other cues that we use to distinguish these two "smells" as being distinct?

   Ans: Sight is a common sense used to help identify 'smell'. The red 'cherry' or the white 'almond' smell are examples of this.

EXERCISE 26
EYE AND VISION

INTRODUCTION

The anatomy and physiology of the eye is fascinating to students. The separation of the eye into anterior and posterior cavities with the anterior cavity further divided into the anterior and posterior chambers is a classification not followed by all authors. The posterior cavity is sometimes known as the vitreous chamber.

The stereoscopic or binocular vision occurring in humans is unusual in mammals. Primates and carnivores are the two orders that have well-adapted binocular vision. Most other mammals have reduced binocular vision but a greater visual field.

In measuring the visual acuity it is important that students do this in pairs. Some students will examine the Snellen eye chart alone and try to determine their visual acuity to avoid embarrassment. The effective use of the opthalmoscope is limited in this lab as the pupils constrict in response to the bright light of the scope. Normally atropine is used to dilate the eye during an exam. In this part of the exercise students can see the vascular nature of the posterior surface of the eye.

Color blindness is another area where students should work in pairs. It is also important to be sensitive to colorblind individuals. If they are willing to examine the charts before a group of students a dramatic understanding can be had as to the role of the cones of the eye.

TIME 2-3 hours

MATERIALS

Models and charts of the eye
Snellen charts
Astigmatism charts
Sharp pencil or fine probe (1 per student pair)
Vision Disk (Hubbard) or large protractor
Microscopes (1 per student or per student pair)
Prepared microscope slides of eye in sagittal section (1 per student pair)
Preserved sheep or cow eyes (1 per student pair)
Dissection trays (1 per student pair)
Dissection gloves - sm, med, lrg box per lab (latex or plastic)
Scalpel or razor blades (1 per student pair)
3by5 inch cards (1 per student pair)
Ishihara color book or colored yarn
Ruler (approximately 35 cm) (1 per student pair)
Rubber squeeze bulb (1 per student pair)
Opthalmoscope and batteries (1 per student pair)
Penlight (1 per student pair)
Desk lamp with 60-watt bulb (1 per student pair)

Paper card with a simple colored image (red circle, blue triangle) printed on it

REVIEW ANSWERS

1. Eye shine in nocturnal mammals is different from the "red eye" seen in some flash photographs. Eye shine is the reflection from the tapetum lucidum. What might "red eye" be due to?

   Ans: The condition called 'red eye' is due to bright light reflecting off of the back of the retina.

2. Fill in the following illustration with the appropriate terms.

   a. Sclera *b. Choroid*

   c. Retina *d. Optic nerve*

   e. Anterior chamber *f. Lens*

3. Since the lens is made of protein, what effect might the preserving fluid used in lab have on the structure of the lens? How would this affect the clarity?

   Ans: In preserved specimens the normally clear lens is denatured and becomes opaque due to the preserving fluid. The protein molecules unwind as they denature and this leads to refraction of the light.

4. What is the consensual reflex of the pupil?

   Ans: The consensual reflex is the increase or decrease of one pupil when the other pupil is exposed to a respective decrease or increase in light.

5. How does the vitreous humor differ from the aqueous humor in terms of location and viscosity?

   Ans: Vitreous humor is located in the posterior cavity and is more viscous (thicker) than aqueous humor. Aqueous humor is located in the anterior cavity and is more watery.

EXERCISE 27
EAR, HEARING, AND EQUILIBRIUM

INTRODUCTION

Try to keep the room as quiet as possible during the hearing tests. You may want to coordinate the lab activity so that the hearing tests can be done all at one time during the lab period. This will limit the amount of noise which can have an effect on the results of the test. In performing the Weber and Rinne test it is important that students know how to strike a tuning fork. They should hold the handle and let the tines vibrate freely. When performing the sound location test, make sure that students strike the tuning fork at the location where the sound is to be determined. If the fork is struck in one area and moved to another, the subject will easily locate the sound.

TIME 2 hours

MATERIALS

Models and charts of the ear (1 per student pair)
Microscopes (1 per student pair)
Slides of the cochlea (1 per student pair)
Tuning fork (256 Hz) (1 per student pair)
Rubber reflex hammer (1 per student pair)
Audiometer (if available) (1 per student pair)
Model of ear ossicles
Meter stick (1 per student pair)
Ticking stopwatch (1 per student pair)

REVIEW ANSWERS

1. Background noise affects hearing tests. In the ticking watch test, what kind of result, in terms of auditory sensitivity, would you have recorded if moderate background noise was present?

   Ans: The subject would not have been able to perceive the ticking sound as easily therefore the test would indicate more hearing loss than was actually present.

2. In the Weber test, the ear that perceives the sound as being louder is the deaf ear. Why is this the case?

   Ans: Conduction deafness leads to an increased sensitivity of the cochlear apparatus which picks up sound from vibration through the skull bones. Vibrations pass through the skull to the temporal bone. The hearing impaired ear would be more sensitive to this perception of sound than an ear where sound is transmitted through the tympanic membrane and ear ossicles.

3. Fill in the following illustration of the ear.

   a. Semicircular canals (ducts) — *b. Cochlea*
   c. Auditory tube — *d. Middle ear (ossicles)*
   e. Tympanic membrane — *f. External auditory meatus (canal)*

4. Fill in the following illustration of the cross section of cochlea.

   a. Scala vestibuli — *b. Vestibular membrane*
   c. Tectorial membrane — *d. Hair cells*
   e. Scala media (cochlear duct) — *f. Scala tympani*

EXERCISE 28
ENDOCRINE SYSTEM

INTRODUCTION

The recent, popular use of hormones such as melatonin, DHEA, and anabolic steroids has brought endocrinology out of the lab and into public view. A discussion of feedback loops and the dangers of unregulated hormone use is very appropriate for the lab. This exercise focuses mostly on the anatomy of the endocrine glands though there is a section on the detection of HCG in urine.

Obtaining urine from pregnant females for a pregnancy test can be a bit of a challenge from time to time. I have found that many women are willing to donate urine "for the cause" and I have frozen these samples in small batches which can last for a few years. Home pregnancy tests have become very reliable in the past few years. As with the handling of all bodily fluids, students should wear protective gloves and treat the material as if it was potentially pathenogenic.

TIME 2 hours

MATERIALS

Models and charts of endocrine glands

Microscopes

Microscope slides of thyroid, pituitary, adrenal gland, pancreas, testis, ovary

Urine samples from a nonpregnant and/or a pregnant individual-25 mls

Pregnancy test kit

Disposable gloves (latex or plastic) and biohazard container

REVIEW ANSWERS

1. Label the endocrine glands indicated in the following illustration.

a. Thyroid gland

b. Parathyroid gland

c. Thymus

d. Adrenals gland

e. Pancreas

f. Ovaries

g. Testes

2. Identify the parts of the pituitary as seen in the following illustration and list 2 hormones located in each.

a. Posterior pituitary

1. oxytocin

2. antidiuretic hormone

b. Anterior pituitary

(any two of the following)

growth hormone

thyroid stimulating hormone

follicle stimulating hormone

luteinizing hormone

prolactin

adrenocorticotropin

3. Identify the three layers of the adrenal cortex as illustrated and list the hormones produced by each layer.

a. Zona reticularis	*glucocorticoids & sex hormones*
b. Zona fasciculata	*glucocorticoids*
c. Zona glomerulosa	*mineralocorticoids*

4. Interstitial cell produce which hormone?

   Ans: Testosterone

5. What structures are responsible for the production of estrogen?

   Ans: The ovarian follicles, corpus luteum and placenta

6. What hormone causes an increase in calcium levels in the blood?

   Ans: Parathyroid hormone

EXERCISE 29
BLOOD CELLS

INTRODUCTION

In this exercise students learn about the various types of formed elements in blood by either making and then staining a blood smear or by examining prepared slides of blood. It is very important that students understand the significance of blood transmitted diseases if they work on fresh human blood or fresh mammalian blood. Students need to be reminded that if they puncture their skin to get blood they need to cover that wound securely. Students should place all biohazard material in the biohazard container or bleach container after they have prepared the blood smear.

If time is limited, using prepared blood slides eliminates the time required for the preparation of blood smears. Some specially prepared blood smears have higher numbers of eosinophils or basophils that can be used as demonstration slides for differential leukocyte counts. Recognition of specific leukocytes can be validated if the average values from the leukocyte count are correct. Students that examine normal blood and determine the basophil count to be 20% are probably counting lymphocytes as basophils.

Make sure that the lab is clean before the students leave. They should wipe any blood from the microscope objective lenses with lens cleaner and lens paper and dispose of the paper in the biohazard container. Make sure that students do not leave glass or blood on the lab tables. Use a 10% bleach solution and a towel to clean off the lab table.

TIME 2-3 hours

MATERIALS

Prepared slides of human blood with Wright's or Geimsa stain
Compound microscopes (1 per student or per student pair)
Lab charts or illustrations showing the various blood cell types
Hand counter (1 per student pair)
Blood staining materials

Dropper bottle of Wright's stain (6 per lab)
Large finger bowl or staining tray (1 per student pair)
Toothpicks (1 small vial per student pair)
Clean microscope slides (1 set per student pair)
Coverslips (1 set per student pair)
Squeeze bottle of distilled water or phosphate buffer solution (1 per table)
Pasteur pipette and bulbs (1 per student pair)
Sterile cotton balls (1 small jar per table)
Alcohol swabs (1 per student)
Sterile, disposable lancets (1 per student)
Biohazard bag or container
Sharps container
10% bleach container

Adhesive bandages
Latex or plastic gloves
Paper towels

REVIEW ANSWERS

1. In counting 100 leukocytes you are accurately able to distinguish 15 basophils. Is this a normal number for the white blood cell count, and what possible health implications can you draw from this?

   Ans: No this number is too high. The normal basophil count is less than 1%. This might indicate an allergic reaction or exposure to radiation.

2. What is the function of the thrombocytes of the blood?

   Ans: The thrombocytes serve to aid in clotting.

3. What percent of the blood volume are formed elements?

   Ans: Formed elements comprise approximately 45% of the blood volume.

4. How does hematopoiesis differ from erythropoiesis?

   Ans: Hematopoiesis is blood formation in general while erythropoiesis is the formation of red blood cells.

5. Label the blood cells in the following illustration.

   a. Erythrocyte
   b. Eosinophil
   c. Lymphocyte
   d. Neutrophil

EXERCISE 30
BLOOD TESTS AND TYPING

INTRODUCTION

The previous exercise involved the examination of blood and the determination of the relative numbers of leukocytes. This exercise is a continuation of the study of blood but concerns ABO and Rh typing along with hematocrit determination and erythrocyte counts.

Blood typing is relatively easy except that the Rh typing can be problematic. Granulations are seen if the antisera is fresh but difficult to determine if the anti-sera warmed during shipment or has been in storage too long.

Sterilized blood is available from some biological supply companies but the number of intact red cells in sterilized blood is reduced to less than a third of those found in fresh blood. I like to do a comparison of student results with both sterilized human blood and fresh mammalian blood with regards to packed cell volume (hematocrit) and erythrocytes/mm^3. The sterilized blood has a hematocrit of 15% or less and a count of around 1.5 million erythrocytes per cubic millimeter. Fresh blood has a hematocrit around 45% and a corresponding count of about 5 million erythrocytes per cubic millimeter. The process of sterilization lyses many of the erythrocytes.

Problems with accurate readings may occur if students put too little or too much blood in the capillary tubes. Another problem lies in the fine glass etchings on the hemacytometer which are difficult to bring into focus for some students.

Make sure that the lab is clean before the students leave. They should wipe any blood from the microscope objective lenses with lens cleaner and lens paper and dispose of the paper in the biohazard container. Make sure that students do not leave glass or blood on the lab tables. Use a 10% bleach solution and a towel to clean off the lab table.

TIME 1.5 hours

MATERIALS

5 mls of fresh, nonhuman mammal blood (dog, sheep, or cow)
Sterilized human blood in vials labeled 1 to 4
(Carolina #K3-70-0120 or other supply company)
(can be used for 2 labs during the same week if needed)
Blood typing antisera (anti-A, anti-B, anti-D), test cards, and toothpicks
(can be used for 2 labs during the same week if needed)
Rh warming tray
Heparinized blood microcapillary tubes (2 per student)
Capillary tube centrifuge
Hematocrit reader (Criticorp, Micro-hematocrit tube reader,
Damon Micro-capillary reader, or mm ruler)
Seal-ease (R) capillary clay (1 per table)
Hemacytometer, coverglass (1 per student pair)

Microscope

Unopette reservoirs (Becton-Dickinson #5850) (2 per student)

Unopette capillary pipettes (10 microliter capacity) (2 per student)

Latex or plastic gloves (1 box each of small, medium, and large)

Contamination bucket with autoclave bag

Container with 10% household bleach solution

Sharps container

REVIEW ANSWERS

1. A person has antibody A and antibody B in his or her blood with no Rh antibody. What specific blood type would this person have?

   Ans: O negative

2. A total of 240 erythrocytes are counted in the hemacytometer chamber. What would be the red blood cell count of this individual in terms of erythrocytes per cubic milliliter?

   Ans: The red blood cell count would be 2,400,000 cells/mm^3.

3. An individual with blood type "B negative" is injected with type A positive blood. What would happen after the injection?

   Ans: The individual with B negative blood carries "A" antisera and possibly anti-Rh antisera. The blood would probably agglutinate and cause a thrombus (clot).

4. What is the normal hematocrit for a healthy female?

   Ans: The normal hematocrit for a female is from 37 to 48%.

5. How might changes in the Unopette technique alter the final determined value of erythrocytes?

   Ans: The values for erythrocyte numbers might be altered by pulling in too much blood or not enough blood in the capillary tube, by not flushing the capillary tube prior to filling the hemacytometer, or by ejecting too much blood into the hemacytometer.

6. Using the following illustration calculate the hematocrit of the individual. Determine if it falls within normal limits.

   Ans: The hematocrit of this individual is 38% and is within normal limits for a female and on the anemic side for a male.

EXERCISE 31
STRUCTURE OF THE HEART

INTRODUCTION

Sheep hearts are reasonable surrogate material for human hearts. The main difference is the location of the anterior and posterior vena cavae in sheep hearts which varies from those of the superior and inferior vena cavae in human hearts. As with all preserved material some students may be sensitive to formaldehyde. Headaches or shortness of breath are common symptoms.

Students sometimes have difficulty in determining which vessel is which in the heart. By placing a probe into a vessel students can determine which chamber it enters. If the probe enters the right atrium then the vessels must be either the anterior or posterior vena cavae. If the probe enters the right ventricle then the vessel must be the pulmonary trunk. If the probe enters the left atrium then the probe passes through the pulmonary veins and if it enters the left ventricle then the probe is in the ascending aorta.

TIME 1.5 hours

MATERIALS

Models and charts of the heart
Preserved sheep hearts (1 per student pair)
Preserved human hearts (if available)
Blunt probes (mall probes) (4 per student pair)
Dissection pans (1 per student pair)
Razor blades or scalpels (1 per student pair)
Sharps container
Disposable gloves (1 box each of small, medium and large)
Waste container
Microscopes (1 per student or student pair)
Prepared slides of cardiac muscle (1 per student pair)

REVIEW ANSWERS

1. What adaptation do you see in the walls of the left ventricle being thicker than those of the right ventricle?

   Ans: The left ventricle pumps blood throughout the body while the right ventricle only pumps blood to the lungs nearby. The force needed to pump blood a greater distance reflects the thicker walls of the left ventricle.

2. How does cardiac muscle resemble skeletal muscle?

   Ans: Cardiac muscle resembles skeletal muscle in that the fibers are striated. This is due to the regular arrangement of the myofilaments.

3. In terms of function, how is cardiac muscle different from skeletal muscle?

   Ans: Cardiac muscle is different from skeletal muscle in that cardiac muscle, as intact tissue, can contract independently from neural impulses. This is not true of skeletal muscle.

4. Label the following illustration.

a. Interatrial septum

b. Left atrium

c. Chordae tendineae

d. Left ventricle wall

e. Interventricular septum

f. Apex

g. Right atrium

h. Right ventricular wall

EXERCISE 32
ELECTRICAL CONDUCTIVITY OF THE HEART

INTRODUCTION

Students need to think of the ECG as the electrical activity of the heart and not the muscular events of the heart. It may take some time to run students through the ECG machine. I find it beneficial to teach the first group how to operate the machine and then have them teach the next group. I listen to hear if the procedures are being followed and come over to assist from time to time.

TIME 2 hours

MATERIALS

Electrocardiograph machine, physiograph, or other ECG recording device
Cot or covered lab table (1 per ECG machine)
Alcohol swabs (1 per student)
Electrode jelly, paste, or saline pads (1 set per student)
Watch with accuracy in seconds (1 per student pair)
Dissection tray (1 per student pair)
Squeeze bottle of water (1 per student pair)
Scissors or razor blade (1 per student pair)
Fresh or thawed sheep heart (1 per student pair)
Clamp (hemostat) or string (1 per student pair)

REVIEW ANSWERS

1. Fibrillation is uncoordinated cardiac muscle contraction. Predict what an ECG would look like if there was no uniform conduction of electrical activity in the heart. Draw what it might look like.

   Ans: Student should show an erratic tracing.

2. What consequence does fibrillation have for cardiac muscle contraction and for the pumping efficiency of the heart? Which is more serious atrial or ventricular fibrillation?

   Ans: Random contraction of the cardiac muscle would result in numerous loci of contraction. With the atria firing at different rates than the ventricles the heart chambers would be potentially antagonistic to one another thus significantly reducing the efficiency of the heart. As the ventricles are the power pumps of the heart, ventricular fibrillation is more serious.

3. What is the "pacemaker" of the heart called?

   Ans: The pacemaker of the heart is the sinoatrial node.

4. If a myocardial infarct (heart attack) destroyed a portion of the right or left bundle branches, what potential change might you see in an ECG?

   Ans: If the bundle branches were damaged then the portion of the ECG that electrically measured the events of the bundle branches would be altered as well. This would be seen as an increase in the time of the QRS interval.

5. Tape or paste your ECG in the following space. Label the P wave, the QRS complex, and the T wave.

EXERCISE 33
FUNCTIONS OF THE HEART

INTRODUCTION

In this lab, heart sounds are correlated with the closure of valves. The resting pulse rate is measured in this exercise (the pulse rate after physical activity will be measured in Exercise 41). Additional effects of cardiac physiology can be determined by the addition of various drugs to the external heart wall of a frog.

The use of live animals to demonstrate physiological principles can be objectionable to some students. If you know that a student is particularly bothered by the sacrifice of animals you may want to offer them an alternative exercise. Even though the demonstration of single pithing frogs versus double pithing has potential for understanding spinal reflexes I have found that it is better for me to prepare the specimens away from students and bring in the animals already doubly pithed.

TIME 2 hours

MATERIALS

Heart sounds and pulse rate:

Clock or watch with second hand
Stethoscope (1 per student pair)
Alcohol wipes (1 per student)

Frog heart experiment:

Frogs (1 per student pair)
Clean dissection instruments
- Scissors
- Razor blades or scalpels
- Dissection tray

Small heart hook (fish hook, copper wire, or Z wire)
Pins
Thread
Frog board
Myograph transducer
Physiology recorder (computer, physiograph or duograph)
Frog Ringer's solution (room temperature, 37° C, and iced)

Solutions:

2% calcium chloride solution
0.1% acetylcholine chloride solution
0.1% epinephrine solution
Saturated caffeine solution

REVIEW ANSWERS

1. Beta-adrenergic blockers are those that bind to norepinephrine sites, preventing these neurotransmitters from having an effect. What effect would the use of "beta blockers" have on heart rate?

   Ans: As norepinephrine increases heart rate, the blocking of norepinephrine would cause a decrease in the heart rate.

2. When would a murmur occur in the lubb/dupp cycle if the AV valves were not properly closing?

   Ans: If the AV valves did not properly close the murmur would be in the lubb sound.

3. What causes the plateau phase of cardiac muscle contraction?

   Ans: The plateau phase of the cardiac muscle cycle is due to the opening of the slow calcium channels in cardiac muscle.

4. How much of a change in the heart rate of the frog did you see after the addition of calcium chloride?

   Ans: This is determined by experimentation. The addition of calcium should slow the heart rate.

What was the change in the contraction strength?

Ans: You should see an increase in contraction strength.

What process might account for this in terms of cardiac muscle interactions with calcium?

Ans: Calcium flows into the cell increasing the time of the plateau phase and calcium serves to remove troponin from the myofibrils increasing contraction strength.

EXERCISE 34
INTRODUCTION TO THE BLOOD VESSELS AND ARTERIES OF THE UPPER BODY

INTRODUCTION

This exercise begins with cross sectional views of arteries and veins. The difference in thickness between the vessels can be applied to either the cadaver or the cat during dissection, as arteries tend to be thicker walled than veins. The cat dissection takes time to do properly and students should take care not to cut organs that they will need to study in later exercises.

Students need to be able to trace the flow of blood from one vessel to another. They may wish to draw a schematic diagram for particular regions of the body illustrating the blood flow from one artery to the next.

TIME 3 hours

MATERIALS

Microscopes
Prepared slides of arteries and veins
Models of the blood vessels of the body
Charts and illustrations of the arterial system
Cats
Dissection equipment:

- Dissection tray or pan
- Scalpels
- Pins
- Blunt probes
- Gloves
- Scissors or bone cutter
- String
- Forceps
- Plastic bag with label

REVIEW ANSWERS

1. Label the following illustration with the major arteries of the body. Try to complete the illustration first and then review the material in this exercise to determine your accuracy.

    a. Right subclavian artery

    b. Ascending aorta (at the junction of the aortic arch)

    c. Right ulnar artery

    d. Left internal carotid artery

    e. Left axillary artery

    f. Left brachial artery

    g. Right radial artery

2. Working in pairs, have your lab partner select an artery for you to name. Quiz each other on the material learned in this exercise.

    To be done as an independent exercise

3. Blood from the left subclavian artery would flow into what vessels as it moves towards the left arm?

    Ans: Blood from the left subclavian artery would next flow into the left axillary artery.

4. Blood in the radial artery comes from what blood vessel?

    Ans: Blood from the radial artery comes from the brachial artery.

5. An aneurysm is a weakened, expanded portion of an artery. Ruptured aneurysms can lead to rapid blood loss. Describe the significance of an aortic aneurysm versus a digital artery aneurysm.

    Ans: The loss of blood in a digital artery aneurysm rupture would be minimal due to the small size of the artery of a finger and the fact that the finger is not a vital organ. On the other hand the rupture of the aorta would be fatal as the vessel is very large and rapid blood loss would follow.

6. The pulmonary arteries carry deoxygenated blood from the heart to the lungs. Umbilical arteries carry a mixture of oxygenated and deoxygenated blood. Why are these blood vessels called arteries?

    Ans: An artery is defined as a vessel that carries blood away from the heart and not by what kind of blood is contained within the vessel. The pulmonary and umbilical arteries are called arteries because they carry blood away from the heart though both carry deoxygenated blood.

EXERCISE 35
ARTERIES OF THE LOWER BODY

INTRODUCTION

This exercise is a continuation of the study of the arteries of the body. If students study the human arterial pattern first, they can then apply this knowledge to the cat as a study specimen. As with the previous exercise, schematic diagrams help students understand the blood flow through the arteries. The branches of the celiac artery are difficult to locate and can more easily be seen if the diaphragm is cut away from the ribs on the left side of the body. Students should be reminded of proper dissection technique and to place all waste material in the appropriate containers.

TIME 2 hours

MATERIALS

Microscope
Prepared slide of arteriosclerosis
Models of the blood vessels of the body
Charts and illustrations of arterial system
Cadaver, if available
Dissection equipment
- Dissection tray or pan
- Scalpels
- Pins
- Blunt probes
- Gloves
- Scissors or bone cutter
- String
- Forceps
- Plastic bag with label

Cats

REVIEW ANSWERS

1. Blood from the popliteal artery comes directly from what artery?

   Ans: Blood from the popliteal artery comes directly from the femoral artery.

2. Blood from the celiac artery flows into three different blood vessels. What are these vessels?

   Ans: Blood from the celiac artery flows into the splenic artery, the left gastric artery and the common hepatic artery.

3. Blood from the superior mesenteric artery feeds what major abdominal organs?

   Ans: Blood from the superior mesenteric artery feeds the small intestine, the cecum, ascending colon and the first part of the transverse colon.

4. In what part of the arterial wall does cholesterol plaque develop?

    Ans: Cholesterol plaque develops deep to the tunica interna.

5. How do the lower pelvic arteries in humans differ from those in cats?

    Ans: In humans the aorta splits into the common iliac artery which subsequently divides into the external iliac and internal iliac arteries. In cats there is no common iliac artery yet there is a caudal artery.

6. Label the following illustration.

    a. Celiac trunk

    b. Right renal artery

    c. Left internal iliac artery

    d. Right femoral artery

    e. Right popliteal artery

    f. Right tibial artery

EXERCISE 36
VEINS AND FETAL CIRCULATION

INTRODUCTION

When students study the flow of veins they need to trace the blood toward the heart. If students understand that the deep veins typically take on the name of the corresponding artery then the study of veins becomes easier. The cat dissection should involve minimal work if the arteries have already been dissected.

A challenge for students is the hepatic portal system. If the cat has not been triply injected with latex the hepatic portal system needs to be carefully dissected. Once the portal vein enters into the liver, finding the hepatic vein can be difficult as it is a short vessel on the dorsal aspect of the liver.

TIME 3 hours

MATERIALS

Models of the blood vessels of the body
Charts and illustrations of venous system
Cadaver, if available
Dissection equipment
- Dissection tray or pan
- Scalpels
- Pins
- Blunt probes
- Gloves
- Scissors or bone cutter
- String
- Forceps
- Plastic bag with label

Cats

REVIEW ANSWERS

1. Blood from the right axillary vein would next travel to what vessel?

   Ans: Blood from the right axillary vein would next travel to the right subclavian vein.

2. What vessels take blood to the left femoral vein?

   Ans: The vessels that take blood to the left femoral vein are the left deep femoral vein and the left great saphenous vein.

3. What area do the right and left external jugular veins drain?

   Ans: The external jugulars drain the outer region of the head.

4. What is the functional nature of a "portal system," and how does it differ from normal venous return flow?

Ans: A portal system is one that begins in a capillary bed, flows through veins and ends in another capillary bed. This is different from the normal venous flow of traveling from a capillary bed to veins and then to the heart.

5. What major vessels take blood to the hepatic portal vein?

Ans: The major vessels leading to the hepatic portal vein are the superior and inferior mesenteric veins, the splenic and gastroepiploic veins.

6. Label the following illustration.

a. Right brachiocephalic vein

b. Superior vena cava

c. Left cephalic vein

d. Inferior vena cava

e. Left common iliac vein

f. Left great saphenous vein

g. Right femoral vein

h. Left internal jugular vein

i. Right brachial vein

j. Right basilic vein

k. Left internal iliac vein

EXERCISE 37
FUNCTIONS OF VESSELS, LYMPHATIC SYSTEM

INTRODUCTION

It is important to correlate the relationship between the lymph system and the cardiovascular system. Discussion of the difference in thickness of the walls of blood vessels and the pressure that occurs in them can be related to the thickness of the walls of a high pressure hose versus a low pressure hose. An examination of histological sections of an artery, vein and lymph vessel will illustrate the differences. Students can see the blood moving through the capillaries of a living frog which is a fascinating part of this exercise.

Dissections of the lymph system in the cat can produce variable results depending on the age of the specimen. Students should be able to see the spleen fairly easily but the thymus may be hard to locate in older specimens. Some of the lymph nodes may have been removed in previous dissections but there should be some that remain.

TIME 1 - 1.5 hours

MATERIALS

Microscopes
Microscope slides of arteries and veins in cross section
Microscope slides of lymphatics with valves
Charts, diagrams, and models of blood vessels
Torso models
Live grass frog (or similar-sized frog)
Dissection scopes
Paper towels
Small squeeze bottle of water

REVIEW ANSWERS

1. From what you know of the functions of lymph nodes, make a prediction of the difference between lymph entering a node and lymph leaving a node. What materials may be missing from the lymph leaving the node?

   Ans: The lymph is interstitial fluid that has passed into the lymphatics. It carries tissue fluid, cellular debris and microorganisms. Since the function of the lymph node is to cleanse the tissue the lymph traveling to the node should have more cell debris and potential microorganisms than the lymph traveling from the node.

2. Elephantiasis is a disease that may be caused, in some cases, by a parasitic worm blocking the lymphatics. Examine the following illustration and predict where the lymphatic blockage occurs.

   Ans: The blockage occurs in the inguinal region of the left leg, the scrotum and the antecubital region of the left upper extremity.

3. In the analysis of breast cancer, lymph nodes of the axillary region are removed and a biopsy is performed. The removal of the nodes is done to determine if cancer has spread from the breast to other regions of the body. What effect would the removal of lymph nodes have on the drainage of the pectoral region?

   Ans: The removal of lymph nodes on the axillary region would cause edema, or swelling of the pectoral region.

4. Superficial veins contain valves, yet deep veins do not. The deep veins are surrounded by muscles. People who are inactive may have problems with their veins. Can you propose a mechanism by which blood from the deep veins may be returned to the heart? (A mechanism other than standing on your head!)

Ans: One of the mechanisms of increasing venous return to the heart in inactive people is for them to wear support hose. The pressure of the hose functions to squeeze the vessels thus increasing the return flow.

EXERCISE 38
BLOOD VESSELS AND BLOOD PRESSURE

INTRODUCTION

Learning how to take blood pressure is a skill that takes some practice. I frequently find that many students in my classes already know how to take blood pressure and I enlist them to help other students learn the process. The main problem seems to be that a student has to do several activities simultaneously. It is difficult to hear the sounds of Korotkov in a noisy room especially in determining the end point of the diastolic pressure.

Students should also be warned about the dangers of mercury if mercury-filled sphygmomanometers are used. Examine the sphygmomanometers before and after lab for mercury leaks.

TIME 1.5 hours

MATERIALS

Stethoscope (1 per student pair)

Alcohol wipes or isopropyl alcohol and sterile cotton swabs (1 per student)

Sphygmomanometer (1 per student pair)

Watch or clock with accuracy in seconds

REVIEW ANSWERS

1. Emotions have an effect on blood pressure. Predict the blood pressure of an individual who recently had a heated argument with a roommate about rent money.

   Ans: The disagreement with an individual can cause the sympathetic nervous system to stimulate the adrenal glands to secrete epinephrine which serves to cause vasoconstriction of many blood vessels thus elevating the blood pressure.

2. Illness can also affect blood pressure. Illness tends to increase stress responses. Predict the blood pressure of an individual with a sinus headache and postnasal drip.

   Ans: The aggravated condition of pain and irritation also increases the release of epinephrine and causes an elevation of blood pressure.

3. Nicotine and caffeine both elevate blood pressure. Explain how an increase in blood pressure could have a negative effect on the pumping efficiency of the heart.

   Ans: The heart is a biological pump and the outflow pressure increases when the heart has to work against the additional force created by elevated blood pressure. If the elevated blood pressure occurs for a short period of time the heart muscle works harder against the load and then relaxes. If the blood pressure remains elevated for long periods then the heart chamber increases in size and the heart loses efficiency.

4. Record your blood pressure.

   Blood pressure ______________.

   Ans: Determined by experimentation

EXERCISE 39
STRUCTURE OF THE RESPIRATORY SYSTEM

INTRODUCTION

The anatomy of the respiratory system involves both an overview of the gross anatomy and the examination of histological sections. A review of the skeletal anatomy of the skull, particularly the nasal cavity, is beneficial before students perform this lab. Sections of lung (fresh or preserved sheep lungs or preserved human lungs) are of benefit as students sometimes think of the lungs as hollow balloons in the chest cavity.

In discussing the histology of the lung I frequently use the analogy of a wing of a building to distinguish between various parts of the microscopic anatomy. The wing of the building represents the alveolar sac with each room being an alveolus. T central hall, connecting the rooms, represents the alveolar duct.

TIME 2 hours

MATERIALS

Lung models or detailed torso model, including midsagittal section of head
Model of larynx
Microscopes
Prepared microscope slides of lung tissue
Charts and illustrations of the respiratory system
Cats
Dissection equipment (dissection trays and instruments)
Fresh or preserved lungs

REVIEW ANSWERS

1. The nasal cartilages are made of hyaline cartilage. What functional adaptation does cartilage have over bone in making up the external framework of the nose?

   Ans: Bone is strong material adapted to provide support or protection, yet it has a tendency to break. Hyaline cartilage is advantageous over bone in that it maintains the shape of the nose but is flexible. This is important for keeping the breathing passages open but, being subject to contact with the external world, it is capable of bending.

2. The surface area of the lungs in humans is about 70 square meters. How can this be so if the lungs are located in the small space of the thoracic cavity? What role do alveoli play in the nature of surface area?

   Ans: The surface area of a particular region can be increased by adding more inner walls to that region. The alveoli function as microscopic chambers that greatly increase the total surface area of the lung.

3. Emphysema is a destruction of the alveoli of the lungs. What effect does this have on the surface area of the lungs?

   Ans: Emphysema destroys the alveoli of the lungs, decreasing the surface area of the lungs, and reducing the contact surface between the lungs and blood.

4. Fill in the following illustration of the human respiratory system.

a. Nasal cavity

b. Nasopharynx

c. Epiglottis

d. Cricoid cartilage

e. Trachea

f. Superior lobe of right lung

g. Middle lobe of right lung

h. Inferior lobe of right lung

i. Primary bronchus

EXERCISE 40
RESPIRATORY FUNCTION, BREATHING, RESPIRATION

INTRODUCTION

Respiratory physiology is intimately involved with several systems including the respiratory, cardiovascular, and muscular systems. Additional respiratory experiments (such as FEV) are conducted in Exercise 41 (Exercise Physiology).

Communicable diseases can be passed through moist air in a spirometer. It is very important that students exhale only into the equipment. As an instructor it is important that you pay attention to how students are responding to the various exercises. If a student appears dizzy after hyperventilation it is important that he or she recover completely before doing other sections of the lab. If at any time a student is physically uncomfortable with the procedure then that student should stop the experiment and be the recorder for someone else.

Biopac has developed a respiratory module with a direct flow meter. This unit comes as part of the MP30 advanced system and involves initial calibration of the system in a relatively simple procedure. The material is available from:

Biopac Systems, Inc.
42 Aero Camino
Goleta, CA 93117
(805) 685-0066
TIME 2 hours

MATERIALS

Respiration model

Bell jar respiration model
Pulmonary Volume Setup

Respirometer (Collins ® respirometer), handheld spirometers or Biopac ® system
Disposable mouthpieces to fit respirometer or spirometers
Watch or clock with accuracy in seconds
Biohazard bag
Breathing Sounds and Breathing Rate Setup

Medium-sized brown paper sacs (2 gallon) (1 per student)
Stethoscope
Alcohol wipes
Acid-Base Setup (1 setup per table)

Litmus solution (10 g litmus powder in 600 ml water)
NaOH solution (1 N) in dropper bottles
Straws

100 ml Erlenmeyer flasks

Safety glasses

REVIEW ANSWERS

1. What is the approximate percent decrease of vital capacity in the same individual from age 25 to age 75?

   Ans: The vital capacity of an individual decreases by about one third from age 25 to 75.

2. How does the decrease in vital capacity potentially influence an individual's athletic performance or aerobic condition as aging occurs?

   Ans: The decrease in vital capacity reduces the volume of oxygen that can be inhaled with each breath. A decrease in oxygen volume limits the amount of work that can be done thus negatively influencing the athletic performance or aerobic condition of the individual.

3. Using your lecture text try to determine which gas is important in stimulating the breathing reflex in the body. How does this gas relate to your experiment of breathing into the paper bag?

   Ans: Carbon dioxide is very important as an indicator of low oxygen levels in the body. By breathing into the paper bag carbon dioxide levels increase stimulating the reflex to breathe.

4. What is the pressure difference between the external air and the pleural cavity when inhalation just begins?

   Ans: As inhalation begins, the pressure is greater in the external air than in the pleural cavity due to the expansion of the thoracic cage increasing the volume of the pleural cavity. Air moves from regions of higher pressure to regions of lower pressure thus filling the lungs.

5. Calculate the IRV of an individual with a vital capacity of 4,400 ml, an expiratory reserve volume of 1,300 ml and a tidal volume of 500 ml.

   Ans: IRV = VC - (ERV + TV) thus IRV = 4,400 - (1,300 +500) = ***2,600 mls***

6. How does carbon dioxide change the acid-base condition of a solution when present in excess?

   Ans: Carbon dioxide combines with water to produce carbonic acid which subsequently dissociates into a bicarbonate ion and a hydrogen ion. The excess carbon dioxide increases the hydrogen ion concentration thus increasing the acidity of the solution.

EXERCISE 41
PHYSIOLOGY OF EXERCISE

INTRODUCTION

Anytime students have health conditions which prevent them from doing strenuous exercise they should be encouraged not to perform that portion of the lab. They can collect data and assist their lab partners. FEV is a measure of general fitness with the greater percent volume of vital capacity reflecting more elasticity of the lungs.

TIME 1.5 hours (depending on access to respirometers)

MATERIALS

16-inch step
20-inch step
Metronome or clock with second hand
Skin-fold caliper
Exercise bicycle, treadmill, or similar aerobic machine
Respirometer capable of measuring volume and time
Disposable mouthpieces
Chart paper
Tape
Nose clips

REVIEW ANSWERS

1. Record your FEV or the one you measured in lab: _____________

   Ans: Determined by experimentation

2. Does this value fall within normal limits?

   Ans: Determined by experimentation - it should be above 75%

3. What is your personal fitness index or the one measured in lab?

   Ans: Determined by experimentation

4. If the heart rate after 5 minutes of exercise was 70, 68, and 66 beats in the consecutive 30-second trials, what would the personal fitness index be and what condition would that represent?

   Ans: To determine the personal fitness index (PFI) you would use the following formula.

   $$PFI = \frac{\text{Number of seconds of exercise X 100}}{2\text{ (sum of 3 pulse counts)}}$$

   $$PFI = \frac{(60 \times 5 \times 100)}{2(70 + 68 + 66)} = \frac{30{,}000}{408} = 73.5 \text{ (high average physical condition)}$$

5. In figure 41.3 the experiment was conducted with a 13.5-liter respirometer. Calculate the FEV of this individual.

   Ans: The FEV_1 is approximately 81%. This is an FEV from an individual with no restricted breathing.

EXERCISE 42
ANATOMY OF THE DIGESTIVE SYSTEM

INTRODUCTION

The anatomy of the digestive system can be conveniently divided into two parts, the alimentary canal and the accessory organs. Many students already know the sequence of the alimentary canal but I like to introduce the major regions which provides an organizational framework from which students can learn. For practical purposes the gross anatomy is generally covered first while examining models, charts, cadavers and cats and the histology is covered as a separate unit using the microscopes.

The digestive tract of the cat is proportionally shorter than that of humans because cats are carnivores and their food has higher food value. Cats do not have an appendix and their liver has multiple lobes whereas there is an appendix in humans and a four-lobed liver. The body cavity should be open from the studies of the circulatory system and the respiratory system.

TIME 3 hours

MATERIALS

Models, charts, or illustrations of the digestive system
Mirror
Cats
Dissection trays
Pins
Scalpels or razor blades
Latex gloves
Waste container
Skull, human teeth, or cast of teeth
Cadaver (if available)
Microscopes
Microscope slides:
- Esophagus
- Stomach
- Small intestine
- Large intestine
- Liver

REVIEW ANSWERS

1. Stomach acidity is in the range of pH 1 to 2. What possible benefits could this have in terms of growth of ingested bacteria?

   Ans: Most bacteria do not grow well in acidic conditions. The pH of 1 to 2 in the stomach acts as a microbial inhibitor killing some microbes outright and inhibiting others from increasing in numbers.

2. Trace the flow of bile from the liver to the duodenum listing all of the structures that come into contact with the bile on its journey.

Ans: Bile from the liver flows through the left and right hepatic ducts to the common hepatic duct before entering the cystic duct. Once in the cystic duct the bile flows into the gall bladder where it is stored. When the gall bladder contracts, the bile flows back out the cystic duct to the common bile duct and into the duodenum.

3. How does the large intestine differ from the small intestine in terms of length?

Ans: The large intestine is about 1.4 meters (4-5 feet) long while the small intestine is about 5 meters (17 feet) long.

4. How does the large intestine differ from the small intestine in terms of diameter?

Ans: The Large intestine is so named because it is larger in diameter. The large intestine is about 7 centimeters (3 inches) in diameter while the small intestine is about 3-4 centimeters (1.5 inches) in diameter.

5. Name two functions of the pancreas.

Ans: One of the functions of the pancreas is to provide digestive enzymes including those that digest proteins, carbohydrates and lipids while another function of the pancreas is to secrete a solution that buffers stomach acid.

6. Label the following illustration.

a. Tongue *b. Oral cavity* *c. Esophagus*
d. Parotid gland *e. Liver* *f. Stomach*
g. Duodenum *h. Small intestine* *i. Ascending colon*
j. Vermiform appendix *k. Sigmoid colon* *l. Rectum*

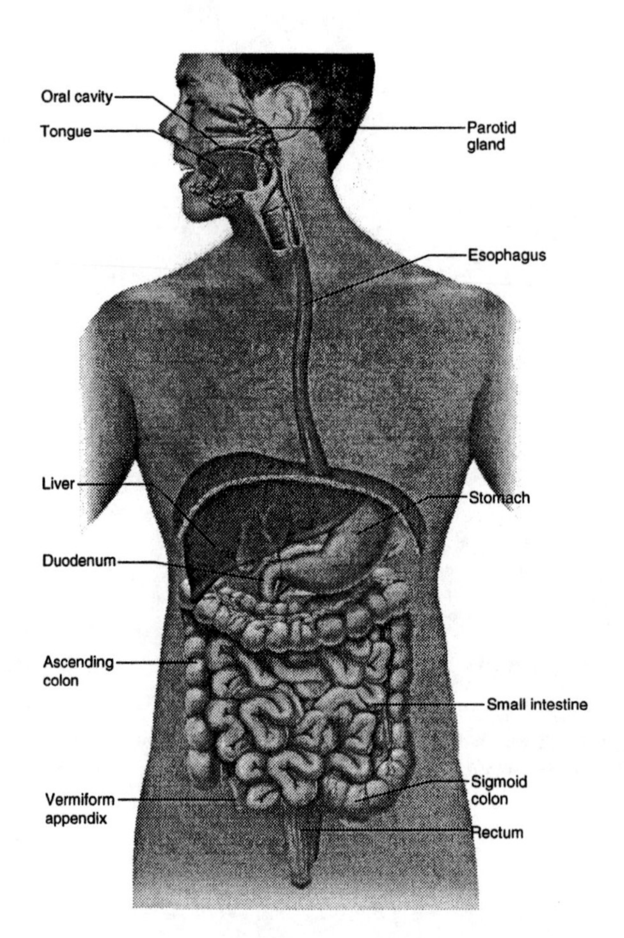

EXERCISE 43
DIGESTIVE PHYSIOLOGY

INTRODUCTION

The physiology of digestion exercise is a lab that requires a fair amount of laboratory preparation. Be sure to order the materials needed in advance. Pancreatin can be stored frozen until ready to use. The enzyme solution should be mixed fresh on the day it is to be used.

Proteins are notoriously hard to digest in a three hour lab. You may want to mix a pancreatin and albumin solution the day before and test for proteins during the lab. Cellulose was added to this experiment to provide a negative result in the test of the effectiveness of digestive enzymes. The role of fiber and other non-digestible materials can be used as a point of discussion after students study the cellulose section.

Some students have difficulty understanding the nature of a positive result and a negative result. In the sugar tests, a positive test indicates the digestion of starch. In the iodine test a positive test indicates that not all the starch was digested.

TIME 3 hours

MATERIALS

144 15 ml test tubes
12 test tube brushes and soap
Warm water bath, set at 35° to 40° C with test tube racks
Hot plates and 400 ml beakers for hot bath (80° to 100° C)
12 test tube holders
#4 cork borer
Small rod to push through the borer
Boxes of microscope slides (1 per table) and equal number of coverslip boxes
6 mortars and pestles
2 bread boards for potato experiment
2 large potatoes per class
12 wax pencils (china markers)
12 pair of goggles (during use of NaOH)
24 5 ml pipettes
24 pipette pumps
12 15 cm rulers
10 250 ml beakers to pour from stock bottle for distribution
Solutions - See Appendix A

0.5% Starch solution
Iodine solution
1% pancreatin solution, fresh

1% glucose solution
Benedict's reagent
Cellulose
Albumin solution
Biuret solution
Litmus cream
Acid solution
1% sodium hydroxide solution

REVIEW ANSWERS

1. Explain why a negative iodine test for starch would indicate a positive result for the enzymatic degradation of starch by pancreatin.

   Ans: The process of starch digestion by pancreatin begins with starch as the substrate. If pancreatin has active amylase enzymes then starch is converted to sugar. Thus a degradation of starch by the enzyme would mean that no starch was left. Starch is tested for by the use of iodine and if the iodine test is negative then starch was digested.

2. What would a positive iodine test indicate in the preceding reaction?

   Ans: A positive iodine test would indicate that not all of the iodine was digested. It could mean that none of the starch was digested or that some of the starch was digested but some was left which reacted with the iodine.

3. Record all your negative results. Determine if these negative results indicate digestion or no digestion.

   Ans: Determined by experimentation

4. Explain why cellulose could or could not be digested by pancreatin.

   Ans: Pancreatin cannot digest cellulose because pancreatic enzymes do not fit the configuration of the molecule. Thus pancreatin does not contain cellulase.

EXERCISE 44
URINARY SYSTEM

INTRODUCTION

The major organs of the urinary system are easy to learn but the kidney has many detailed anatomical features that present some difficulties. These histological features, such as the glomeruli, proximal convoluted tubules, and nephron loops among others, have significant functional implications. Other parts of the urinary system, such as the specific regions of the male urethra are covered in the exercises on reproduction (Exercises 46 and 47).

Dissection of the sheep kidney is best performed if a coronal cut is made a little bit off-center of the midline of the kidney. It is here that minor and major calyces are more apparent. Minor and major calyces give some students difficulty. I have used the analogy of minor calyces being small funnels that lead into a larger funnel (the major calyx). Another analogy to compare the major calyces to the renal pelvis is one of a glove in a pocket. The major calyces represent the fingers of the glove while the renal pelvis represents the palm portion of the glove. The space that the glove occupies (the pocket) is represented by the renal sinus.

Some students also have difficulty distinguishing between the blood flow in the kidney and the flow of filtrate in the kidney. Having them draw the blood flow from the renal artery through all of the vessels to the renal vein can be beneficial. They can then trace the flow of the ultrafiltrate from the glomerulus to the collecting duct.

TIME 2 hours

MATERIALS

Models and charts of the urinary system
Models and illustrations of the kidney and nephron system
Microscopes
Microscope slides of kidney and bladder
Samples of renal calculi (if available)
Preserved specimens of sheep or other mammal kidney
Dissection trays and materials

REVIEW ANSWERS

1. Blood in an arcuate vein would next flow into what structure?

   Ans: Blood from the arcuate vein is on the return flow in the kidney and it would next move to the interlobar vein.

2. What physical feature distinguishes a proximal convoluted tubule from a distal convoluted tubule?

   Ans: The proximal convoluted tubule has an inner margin of microvilli called the 'brush border.' The inner margin of the distal convoluted tubule does not have a 'brush border.'

3. Name the four parts of the nephron.

   Ans: glomerular capsule, proximal convoluted tubule, nephron loop, distal convoluted tubule.

4. What type of cell lines the bladder?

   Ans: The type of cell that lines the bladder is transitional epithelium.

5. Fill out the following illustration.

   a. Renal capsule

   b. Renal cortex

   c. Renal pyramid

   d. Renal papilla

   e. Major calyx

   f. Renal pelvis

   g. Ureter

   h. Renal artery

   i. Renal vein

EXERCISE 45
URINALYSIS

INTRODUCTION

The idea of collecting urine at school and analyzing it is initially abhorrent to many students yet they usually have a great appreciation for the exercise at the end of the lab period. As in all of the labs using bodily fluid urine must be treated as a pathogenic material. Students should handle their own urine, wearing gloves, and taking precautions as they would with any bodily fluid.

Provide ample biohazard bags and bleach containers for the proper disposal of all urine-contaminated material. Spills should be cleaned up immediately and the area wiped-down with a 10% bleach solution.

TIME 2 hours

MATERIALS

Sterile urine collection containers
Microscope slides
Coverslips
Urine sediment stain (Sedistain, Volusol, etc.)
Chemstrip or Multistix ® 10SG* urine test strips
Tapered centrifuge tubes
Test tube racks
Pasteur pipettes and bulbs
Centrifuge
Biohazard bag
Microscopes
Urine specimen (yours or synthetic/sterilized urine)
10% bleach solution
* Multistix ® 10 SG - by Bayer, Inc.

REVIEW ANSWERS

1. If you process 180 liters of water through the kidney each day yet produce only 1.8 liters of urine, approximately how efficient are your kidneys at re absorbing the water passing through them?

   Ans: The kidneys are 99% efficient at reabsorbing water.

2. Assume that a person did not collect a midstream sample of urine but collected a sample from the beginning of urination. What additional materials might be in greater numbers in this particular sample?

   Ans: The reason for a midstream sample is to avoid the normal microbial flora that develops in the urethra between urinations. A sample taken at the beginning of urination should have additional bacteria and perhaps yeasts in the urine.

3. List the materials you found in the urine sample.

   Ans: Determined by observation

4. What was the specific gravity of your urine sample?

   Ans: Determined by experimentation

5. How much water do you normally drink each day?

   Ans: Personal data

EXERCISE 46
MALE REPRODUCTIVE SYSTEM

INTRODUCTION

The histology of the testes is covered in Exercise 28 with an examination of the interstitial cells. In this exercise the interstitial cells are studied along with the structure of the seminiferous tubules. Primary spermatocytes are located near the outside of the seminiferous tubules while secondary spermatocytes are located closed to the spermatids.

Determination of the sex of the cat is the initial stage of understanding the reproductive systems. If the male cat is neutered the scrotal sac may not be obvious. The penis in the cat is less obvious than in the human. Students may be unwilling to admit their ignorance of feline sex determination so a casual "walk-through" may be something you want to do to get each group on track. Remind students to dispose of cat waste properly, keeping fur and other cat parts out of the lab sinks.

It is important that the dissection of the vas deferens is done with care. The vas deferens loops over the ureter and should not be cut during the dissection in the pelvic cavity.

TIME 2-3 hours

MATERIALS

Charts, models, and illustrations of the male reproductive system
Microscopes
Prepared slides of a cross section of testis
Cat
Dissection trays and equipment

REVIEW ANSWERS

1. The testes are considered mixed glands because they have both an endocrine and exocrine function. Describe the endocrine and exocrine products that come from the testes.

   Ans: The endocrine function of the testes involves the production of testosterone which is produced by the interstitial cells. The exocrine function of the testes is the production of spermatozoa which is produced by the seminiferous tubules.

2. Male sterility can result from excessively high temperatures around the testes. What mechanism occurs in the scrotum to counteract the effects of high temperature?

   Ans: The dartos muscle is a smooth muscle in the wall of the scrotum that contracts when the temperature near the scrotum is cool. If the temperature is warm then the dartos muscle relaxes and allows the testes to descend away from the body.

3. List all of the structures involved in producing semen.

   Ans: Semen is a fluid that is produced from seminiferous tubules (that make spermatozoa) and secretions from the seminal vesicles, the prostate gland and the bulbourethral glands.

4. How does spermatozoa differ from seminal fluid?

   Ans: Spermatozoa are the sex cells produced by the seminiferous tubules while seminal fluid is the secretions of the seminal vesicles, the prostate gland and the bulbourethral glands. Spermatozoa and seminal fluid are the two components of semen.

5. A vasectomy is the cutting and tying of the two vas deferens at the level of the spermatic cords. Review the percent of spermatozoa that composes semen and determine what effect a vasectomy has on semen volume.

   Ans: As spermatozoa compose less than 1% of the semen a vasectomy has no appreciable effect on reducing semen volume.

6. What male reproductive gland is missing in the cat but present in the human?

   Ans: The seminal vesicles are present in human males but absent in cats.

EXERCISE 47
FEMALE REPRODUCTIVE SYSTEM

INTRODUCTION

The female reproductive system is functionally more complex than the male reproductive system in that it produces gametes, receives male gametes, provides nourishment and a location for the developing fetus and delivers the fetus. A general study of the models of the female reproductive system is a good place to begin the exercise. In addition to determining the path of the oocyte from the ovary to the endometrium students should also note the various ligaments of the female reproductive system.

The histology of the ovary is better seen in cat ovaries than in human ovaries. Cats have multiple births and there tend to be more oocytes at various levels of development in cats than in humans.

As in the previous exercise, students should determine the sex of the cat prior to beginning the dissection. The uterus in cats has two horns which allows more room for multiple births.

TIME 2-3 hours

MATERIALS

Charts, models, and illustrations of the female reproductive system
Microscopes
Prepared slides of ovary and uterus
Dissection trays and equipment
Cat

REVIEW ANSWERS

1. Trace the pathway of milk from the mammary glands to expulsion.

   Ans: The pathway of milk begins with the mammary glands then flows to the lactiferous ducts and finally to the ampullae before exiting through the nipple.

2. Ectopic pregnancies are those that occur outside of the endometrial layer of the uterus. Provide an explanation for how the pregnancies may occur in the uterine tube (thus a tubal pregnancy) or in the abdominopelvic cavity.

   Ans: The development of the placenta occurs under the influence of Human Chorionic Gonadotropin (HCG). This hormone is produced by the developing cell mass (pre-embryo) and causes placental development wherever implantation occurs. If implantation occurs in the uterine tube or even in the abdominopelvic cavity a placenta develops at that place.

3. How does the uterus of the human female differ from that of the cat?

   Ans: The human female has a simple uterus while the uterus of a cat is shaped like a "Y" with two horns.

4. How does the structure of the uterus in the cat correlate to multiple births from each pregnancy?

   Ans: The uterus in a cat is relatively large compared to the overall body size of a cat and this increase in size allows for multiple embryos to develop.

APPENDIX A
MATERIALS NEEDED
PREPARATIONS OF MATERIALS

The preparations below are designed for a lab of 24 students. For the preparation of solution I have found it best to estimate how many mls of stock solutions are required for all of the students in a lab and then double that amount. The preparations are listed alphabetically and are also found in Appendix C at the end of the lab manual. The number of the lab exercise follows the solution description for cross referencing.

Acetylcholine chloride solution 0.1%

Add 0.1 gram of acetylcholine chloride to 100 mls Frog Ringer's solution. Pour into a small, labeled dropper bottle. (Exercise 33)

Acid solution

Pour 200 mls lemon juice or vinegar into dropper bottles labeled "Acid Solution." (Exercise 43)

Agar plates

Add 15 grams agar to enough water to make 1 liter of solution. Boil and stir the agar until it all dissolves. Pour into petri dishes for 3 dishes per table. (Exercise 5)

Albumin solution

Add 10 mls of egg white to 80 mls of water. Blend and strain through cheese cloth. Pour into a bottle and label "Albumin Solution." (Exercise 43)

Benedict's reagent

A copper sulfate solution that turns color if reducing sugars are present and remains blue in the absence of reducing sugars. Add 35 grams sodium citrate and 20 grams sodium carbonate (Na_2CO_3) to 160 mls of water. Filter through paper into a glass beaker. Dissolve 3.5 grams copper sulfate ($CuSO_4$) in 40 mls of water. Pour the copper sulfate solution into the 160 mls stirring constantly. (Exercise 43)

Bleach solution 10%

Mix 100 mls of household bleach (sodium hypochlorite) with 900 mls tap water. (Exercises 29, 30, and 45)

Biuret solution

This solution tests for the peptide bonds in proteins. If peptide bonds are present the solution turns a light pink. First make a 10% Sodium Hydroxide (NaOH) solution by adding 135 mls of water slowly to 15 grams of NaOH. This should make about 150 mls of solution. Stir the mixture carefully. The reaction is exothermic and will generate quite a bit of heat. CAUTION - NaOH is caustic. Wear gloves and goggles. Add to this a 1% copper sulfate ($CuSO_4$) solution (1 gram copper sulfate in 100 mls distilled water) until the color of the mixture is a sky-blue (a pale blue). Pour into two bottles and label the bottles with the warning "Poison" and "Biuret Solution". (Exercise 43)

Caffeine solution, saturated

Add small amounts of caffeine to 50 mls of water until no more will dissolve. Decant the solution into small dropper bottles. (Exercise 33)

Calcium chloride solution 2%

Weigh 5 grams of calcium chloride and place in a graduated cylinder. Add Frog Ringer's solution to make 250 mls. Pour in dropper bottles. (Exercise 33)

Cat wetting solution

Numerous formulations are available for keeping preserved specimens moist. Some commercial preparations are available that reduce the exposure of students to formalin or phenol. You may not need any wetting solution at all if the cats are kept in a plastic bag that is securely tied closed. You can make a wetting solution by putting 75 mls of formalin, 100 mls glycerol, and 825 mls distilled water in a 1 liter squeeze bottle. Another mixture consists of equal parts Lysol and water. (Exercises 13-18)

Cellulose

Cut several (3-4) grams of pure cotton (cotton wool, cotton balls) into fine pieces (0.5 cm or less). Label "Cellulose." (Exercise 43)

Epinephrine solution 0.1%

Add 0.1 gram of adrenalin chloride in 100 mls of Frog Ringer's solution. Label and pour the solution into small dropper bottles. (Exercise 33)

Essential oils preparation

Fill several small, screw-top vials with peppermint, almond, wintergreen and camphor oils (available from local drug stores). Label 'peppermint', 'almond', 'wintergreen' and 'camphor' respectively and keep vials in separate wide-mouthed jars to prevent cross contamination of scent. (Exercise 25).

Fill 4 small vials half-way to the top with cotton and color them red with food coloring. Label the vials "wild cherry" and add benzaldehyde solution until the cotton is moist. (Exercise 25)

Fat testing solution (1% Sudan III solution)

Dissolve 1 gram of Sudan III in 100 mls of absolute alcohol. (Exercise 5)

Filtration solution

(1% starch, charcoal and copper sulfate solution)

Take 5 grams of starch, 5 grams of powdered charcoal and 5 grams of copper sulfate ($CUSO_4$) and place them in a 1 liter beaker. Add enough water to make 500 mls. Stir well and pour into a 500 ml bottle. Label "Filtration solution". (Exercise 5)

Frog Ringer's solution

Weigh and place the following materials in a 1 liter graduated cylinder.

6.5 g NaCl (sodium chloride)
0.2 g $NaHCO_3$ (sodium bicarbonate)

0.1 g $CaCl_2$ (calcium chloride)

0.1 g KCl (potassium chloride)

To these add enough water to make 1000 ml. This solution should be prepared fresh and used within a few weeks. (Exercises 23 and 33. In Exercise 33 there should be 3 solutions prepared - one at room temp, one at 37° C and one in an ice bath.)

Glucose solution 1%

Add 2 grams of glucose (dextrose) in enough water to make 200 mls. Stir until dissolved and pour into 2 clean bottles. Label "1% Glucose Solution." (Exercise 43)

Hydrochloric acid solution 0.1%

Add 1 ml of concentrated HCl to 1 liter of water. (Exercise 23)

Iodine solution

Prepare by adding 10.0 g I_2 (Iodine) and 20.0 g KI (Potassium iodide) to 1 liter of distilled water. Store in small dark dropper bottles. Label "Lugol's Iodine." (Exercises 5 and 43)

Litmus cream

Use approximately 250 mls of heavy cream. To this add powdered litmus until the cream is a light blue. Pour into 2 separate bottles and label "Litmus Cream." (Exercise 43)

Litmus solution

Weigh 10 g Litmus powder and dissolve in 600 mls water. Pour into 2 bottles. (Exercise 40)

Methylene blue 1%

Add 5 g methylene blue powder in 500 ml distilled water. Pour into dropper bottles. (Exercise 3)

Methylene blue solution 0.01 M

Add 3.2 grams methylene blue (MW 320) to distilled water to make 1 liter of solution. Place in dropper bottles. (Exercise 5)

Molasses or concentrated sucrose solution 20%

Use undiluted molasses or a 20% sugar solution. To make the sugar solution add 100 grams of table sugar (sucrose) to water to make 500 mls of solution. Make sure that the sucrose is completely dissolved. (Exercise 5)

Nitric acid 1 N for decalcifying bones

Add 64 mls of concentrated nitric acid (70%) slowly to water to make 1 liter of solution. (Exercise 8)

Pancreatin solution 1%

Place 6 grams of pancreatin in a graduated cylinder and add water to make 600 mls. Stir well. Adjust the pH with 0.05 M Sodium Bicarbonate until neutral (pH 7). Pour into two different stock bottles and label 1% Pancreatin Solution. Preparation note - use fresh pancreatin and not the stuff that has been on the shelf since 1966. Pancreatin may be stored frozen (**not** in a frost-free freezer that regularly cycles between freezing and defrosting). Also note that commercially prepared pancreatin has an optimum pH. If the pH is too low then the reaction will be slowed or stopped. (Exercise 43)

Perfume, dilute solution

Add 10 mls inexpensive perfume to 50 mls of isopropyl alcohol. (Exercise 25)

Phosphate buffer solution

Add 3.3 grams of potassium phosphate (monobasic) and 1.3 grams of sodium phosphate (dibasic) to 500 mls of water. Place in squeeze bottles. (Exercise 29)

Potassium dichromate solution 0.01 M

Add 2.94 grams of Potassium dichromate (MW 294) crystals to water to make 1 liter of solution. Label and pour into dropper bottles. (Exercise 5)

Potassium permanganate solution 0.01 M

Add 1.58 grams of potassium permanganate (MW 158) crystals to water to make 1 liter of solution. Label and pour into dark brown dropper bottles (Exercise 5)

Procaine hydrochloride

Place 1 gram of procaine hydrochloride solution in 1 ml water. Add to this 30 mls of pure ethanol. Place in small screw-capped bottle. (Exercise 23)

Quinine solution (0.5% quinine sulfate solution)

Measure 2.5 grams of pharmaceutical grade quinine sulfate and place it in a clean container. Add 500 mls of water to the quinine sulfate and stir well. Pour into 12 ounce paper cups for lab. (Exercise 25)

Saline solution 0.9% (Physiological saline)

Put 9.0 g NaCl in 1000 ml water and pour into small dropper bottles (Exercise 5)

Saline solution 5%

Add 25 grams of NaCl crystals to water to make 500 mls of solution. Label the solution and place in small dropper bottles. (Exercise 5)

Salt water solution 3%

Add 15 grams of NaCl crystals (Table salt is acceptable) to water to make 500 mls of solution. Pour into 12 ounce paper cups for lab. (Exercise 25)

Sodium chloride solution 5%

Add 2.5 grams of NaCl crystals to water to make 50 mls of solution. Label the solution and place in small beaker. (Exercise 23)

Sodium hydroxide solution 1%

Add water to 2 grams NaOH to make 200 mls of solution. See caution under Biuret solution. Label as "1% NaOH solution." (Exercise 43)

Sodium hydroxide solution 1 Normal

Add 40 grams NaOH crystals or powder to 500 mls of water. Add additional water to make 1 liter of solution. Caution, the reaction is exothermic and will generate heat. Wear protective gloves and eye wear. If you spill this on your skin make sure that you flush your skin immediately with cold water. (Exercise 40)

Starch solution 0.5%

A potato starch solution is made by first boiling 500 mls of water. Remove the water from the hot plate and add 2.5 grams of potato starch powder. Stir and cool the mixture. Do <u>not</u> boil the starch and water mixture as this will lead to some hydrolysis of starch to sugar. Test for the presence of sugar by using the Benedict's reagent. There should be no sugar present. Place into 250 ml bottles and label "0.5% Starch Solution." (Exercise 43)

Starch solution 1%

Boil 1 liter of distilled water. Remove the water from the heat and add 10 g of cornstarch (or 10 g of potato starch). Filter the mixture through cheese cloth into bottles. (Exercise 5)

Sugar solution 3%

Using a clean container, dissolve 15 grams of table sugar in enough water to make 500 mls of solution. Pour into a 12 ounce paper cup for lab. (Exercise 25)

Sugar solutions

Four table sugar solutions of 2 liters each. (Exercise 5)

0% - 2 liters of water

5% - dissolve 100 grams sugar in enough water to make 2 liters of solution

15% - dissolve 300 grams of sugar in enough water to make 2 liters of solution

30% - dissolve 600 grams of sugar in enough water to make 2 liters of solution

Vinegar solution

Use household vinegar or make a 5% acetic acid solution by adding 5 mls of concentrated acetic acid to about 50 mls of water and then adding additional water to make 100 mls. (Exercise 25)

Wright's stain

Wright's stain is available as a commercially prepared solution from a number of biological supply houses. (Exercise 29)

APPENDIX B
SUPPLIERS

This is a list of supply houses that commonly provide equipment and materials used in many anatomy and physiology laboratories. You may be able to find other companies locally or regional offices of the below listed suppliers.

Aldrich Chemical Co., Inc.
940 West Saint Paul Avenue
Milwaukee, WI 53233

American Optical Company
Instrument Division
Buffalo, NY 14215

Beckman Instruments, Inc.
3900 River Rd.
Schiller Park, IL 60176

Becton-Dickson
Parsippany, NJ 07054

Biopac Systems, Inc.
42 Aero Camino
Goleta, CA 93117
(805) 685-0066

Burdick Corporation
Milton, WI 53563

Calbiochem
10933 N. Torrey Pines Road
La Jolla, CA 92037

Carolina Biological Supply Company
Eastern Region
2700 York Road
Burlington, NC 27215
(800) 334-5551
Western Region
Gladstone, OR 97027
(800) 547-1733

Central Scientific Company
2600 S. Kostner Avenue
Chicago, IL 60623

Delta Biologicals
P.O. Box 26666
Tucson, AZ 85726

Denoyer-Geppert Company
5235 Ravenswood Avenue
Chicago, IL 60640

Difco Laboratories
P.O. Box 1058A
Detroit, MI 48232

Edmund Scientific Company
101 E. Gloucester Pike
Barrington, NJ 08007

Fisher Scientific Company
1232 N. Honore Street
Chicago, IL 60622
Many Regional Centers

Flinn Scientific
P.O. Box 219
Batavia, IL 60510

Frey Scientific
905 Hickory Lane, P.O. Box 8101
Mansfield, OH 44901

Gilson Medical Electronics
P.O. Box 27
3000 West Beltline Drive
Middleton, WI 53562

Grass Instrument Company
Quincy, MA 02169

ICN Biochemicals
P.O. Box 28050
Cleveland, OH 44128

Intelitool
P.O. Box 459
Batavia, IL 60510

Narco Bio-Systems
7651 Airport Boulevard
Houston, TX 77061

Nasco, Inc.
901 Janesville Avenue
Fort Atkinson, Wl 53538

Nebraska Scientific
3823 Leavenwortll Street
Omaha, NE 68105

Phipps and Bird, Inc.
303 S. Sixth Street
Richmond, VA 23205

Propper & Sons, Inc.
New Hyde Park, NY 11040

Sargent-Welch Scientific Company
7300 N. Linder Avenue
Skokie, IL 60078

Scientific Products
1210 Waukegan Road
McGraw Park, IL 60085

Sigma Chemical Co.
P.O. Box 14508
St. Louis, MO 63178
(800) 325-3010

Southern Biological Supply
P.O. Box 368
McKenzie, TN 38201

Stryker Corporation
Kalamazoo, MI 49003

Tektronix Company
Tektronix Industrial Park
Beaverton, OR 97005

Turtox/Cambosco
Macmillan Science Company
8200 Hoyne Ave.
Chicago, IL 60620

VWR
P.O. Box 626
Bridgeport, NJ 08014
(800) 234-9300

Ward's Natural Science Establishment, Inc.
P. O. Box 1712
Rochester, NY 14603
(800) 962-2660

Warren E. Collins, Inc.
220 Wood Road
Braintree, MA 02184